BANK job

The Story of C. D. Waggoner

By Peter F. Kenworthy

*To Elizabeth —
my wonderful landlady
while this tale was being
crafted. Enjoy! all love,
Peter
10 - 15-05*

WESTERN REFLECTIONS PUBLISHING COMPANY

Montrose, CO

ISBN-13: 978-1-932738-24-7
ISBN-10: 1-932738-24-X

Library of Congress Control Number: 2005929378

Cover photograph: Walker Art Studio
Cover and text design: Laurie Goralka Design

First Edition
Printed in the United States of America

Western Reflections Publishing Company®
219 Main Street
Montrose, CO 81401
www.westernreflectionspub.com

*To H.L.W., whose love, enthusiasm, and encouragement have been
offered countless times, and, just as often, taken.
To my sons, Hugh, Nick, and Gus. From the history covered in this
story, I hope you will gain even more appreciation for the remarkable
town where you have grown up.
To my mother who taught me so much of what I find
truly useful in life.
To my brothers who always loved the West
and the stories about it.
To Telluride old-timers: those who are still with us,
and those who have gone ahead.*

ACKNOWLEDGMENTS

I wish to thank P. David Smith, my publisher, for inspiring in me the idea to write this tale. Thanks, too, to Midge Carriere for the loan of a chockfull and fascinating scrapbook that was once the property of her mother's friend Sarah Larcher, a laundress for the soiled doves of Pacific Street. I am grateful to the Telluride Council for the Arts and Humanities for a grant that helped cover the cost of a proofreader. I am indebted, too, to my editor, Bonnie Beach, who has schooled me thoroughly in the use of the comma but who, otherwise, has been most tolerant of my attempts to control the English language. Most of all, I want to thank and pay tribute to Alta Cassietto, who gave me just enough inside information about C.D.Waggoner to fuel my imagination, and who showed me the hat pin made with a gold nugget that had once been his — a present to him long ago from her father. I can only hope that I will find myself, if ever I approach her five score years, even half as bright, and full of energy, as Alta is.

CHAPTER ONE

Telluride, Colorado
August, 1929

Buck Waggoner closed the door of the Bank of Telluride behind him and stepped into the dark of the night. The moon had not yet crested the mountains at the eastern end of the canyon and he fumbled for a moment to lock the door, managing at last by feel more than sight. Colorado Avenue was quiet, deserted. He walked slowly down the street toward the post office. Ahead of him, the high, sharp dome of Ajax Mountain was limned faintly by the rising light of the hidden moon. Waggoner turned left on Pine Street. He walked slowly, not because of the darkness: That was of no concern to him. The steps he took were identical to those he had taken virtually every day for the past thirty years. As he walked, he fingered the drafts that he had withdrawn from the bank's vault. They were made out in blank and signed by the bank's cashier, Clarence Downtain. It was Downtain's custom, whenever he left town, to leave Waggoner with a quantity of signed drafts. If, in his absence, the bank needed funds from any of the other banks with which it kept monies on deposit, the drafts could be filled out and negotiated. Once an amount and the name of the depository bank was typed in, all that was required was Waggoner's signature and the draft could be presented for payment.

Downtain was in Denver attending a Knights of Pythos conference. He would be there all week and would take another week of vacation afterward. It was awkward timing. Waggoner had just learned that the bank was going to be visited the day after Downtain's scheduled return by a team of examiners from the state banking commission. The short notice was deliberate. The commissioner, Grant McFerson, was on a crusade to save the Colorado banking system. Waggoner was well aware of McFerson's efforts and activities. Every week for months there had been reports in the newspapers of banks all around the state being shut down or shored up. In Downtain's absence, Waggoner had begun, with his vice president, Will Scanlon, a hasty effort to prepare for the audit. Scanlon's attitude, as usual, had been dismissive.

"Let 'em come," he had snorted. "If we can't talk our way past some pencil-peckers from Denver, we should be shot anyway."

Waggoner shared none of Scanlon's bravado. But then, he never had.

He paused at the corner of Pine and Columbia. Although he couldn't see past the Miners' Union building and the darkened houses in between, he knew that at the far end of the block light was shining from the windows of his house. He knew, too, that his wife would have all in order. It would fall to him to simply load into the Studebaker all that she had packed.

He glanced east, wishing that the moon would hurry. The outline of Ajax was brightening, but the brilliant light that the moon would later cast on it was still a while off. Waggoner hadn't the luxury of time to wait for it.

He crossed the street and the thought that he had been having recurred to him: It was not by chance that the bank had been chosen for examination. McFerson would surely have had news of the Koen case. It would not have been big news in Denver, but it would have been noted. McFerson or someone in his office would have heard about it or read about it. A note would have been scribbled or an article cut from a newspaper and a thought would have begun to germinate. The name "Telluride" — so long ago forgotten that it seemed of no interest to the outside world, to the Denver financial nabobs — would have suddenly resurfaced. Given the context of the Koen case, an inkling would have occurred to McFerson, or a suggestion put to him, that perhaps it would be timely to pay the town a visit.

Waggoner hesitated again halfway up the block. He tilted his head to peer at the vault of stars whose diamantine sparkle had not yet been outshone by the moon.

What Anise had done, Waggoner thought, was foolhardy, even stupid. He could not bring himself to rebuke her, though, even in his own thoughts. Who was he to judge such a thing? What worried him, however, was that McFerson's audit team would assuredly take special interest in any transactions that had involved the indicted assistant county treasurer. Waggoner suspected that they would be at the top of their list. He dropped his head and his shoulders slumped. He was fifty-four years old. For thirty-three years he had worked to keep the

Bank of Telluride successful; to fulfill its leading role in the town's well-being. It seemed now he no longer even knew what that meant. Through no fault of his own, the town was on its knees. Whatever sacrifices he had made, whatever risks taken, they now all seemed for naught. The town was dying.

Opening the front door of his house, Waggoner saw with satisfaction that his wife, indeed, had everything in order. As he had thought she would, Mary had packed too many things. It would surprise him to get all the cases, valises, and portmanteaux that awaited him in a line, snugly strapped, arranged in the Studebaker. He didn't chide her. He was already asking too much of her. He would find a way to fit it all in.

The night was warm and he was damp with sweat by the time he had everything loaded. The back seat and the trunk of the Studebaker were filled, and he had still needed to use the car's rear rack. He considered washing and changing his clothes but decided against it. Now that the time had come to go, he wanted no further delay.

The moon had risen while he worked, and it now washed the night with silver light. He studied his house, resting from his exertions, waiting for Mary. The house was not nearly as grand as those on North Oak Street, two blocks west, but Waggoner thought it quite splendid in its details. Its basic structure was cross-gable, with the high front triangle directly facing and mimicking the peak of Ajax Mountain. The windows, with light now flashing on and off as Mary went from room to room, making a last check for things she had perhaps forgotten to pack, were flanked by routed-out surrounds, and routed-out corner-boards framed the facade. A full-width open porch extended across the front of the house, its design Victorian gingerbread. The spindle-work porch supports, the beading along the eave ends, acorn pendils, turned balusters, and the scroll and bracket details in the trim work had all long drawn the admiring regards of passersby. Waggoner had always made certain that the intricacy of the details was shown off to best effect by the way the house was painted, using, in all, eight different colors, though most of them were confined to highlights and flourishes. The main colors of the house were variations of green and gold —appropriate colors for the president of the town's only bank.

The last of the lights in the house went out and Mary was at the front door, locking it. Waggoner climbed the steps of the front porch and then helped his wife back down them. He walked her to the car and held the door as she got in. As he passed around the car to the driver's side, his eyes swept the high jagged skyline surrounding the town on three sides. The peaks and ridges of the mountains soared to over twelve and thirteen thousand feet. In the wash of moonlight, the drama of their pitch and height was accentuated. Waggoner loved the mountains. In thirty years he had never tired of studying them, exploring them, living in them. Unlike some, he had never taken them for granted nor underestimated the rigor of survival in their midst. He was a lowlander by birth, from the plains of Illinois. No matter where he came from, though, nor how far away he might end up, there was room for nowhere else in his heart but the awe-inspiring San Juan Mountains.

Waggoner slid behind the big steering wheel of the Studebaker and turned the ignition. The engine cranked with a slow throbbing hum then caught, its cylinders firing evenly. Mary put her hand on her husband's arm but said nothing. In equal silence, he patted her hand then put the car into gear and drove down the street.

❀ ❀ ❀

Alta Cassietto lived across the street and down the block from the Waggoners. Her house was flanked by those of the Wunderlichs' and Harry Miller's, the barber. Her home was smaller than theirs and she had less of a yard, most of which was kept grass-free by two large spruce trees that dropped a profusion of needles and blocked the sun. The little house had belonged to her parents, who had met at the Gold King Mine and married in 1905. Alta was born two years later in Cedaredge, where her parents had tried to start a small farm. The venture proved unsuccessful and, within a year, they sold out and went back to Italy. Their luck was no better in the homeland than it had been abroad, and the political atmosphere was choked with the threat of war. In 1914, Alta's parents moved back with her to America, all the way back to Telluride, and she started school speaking not a word of English.

That had changed quickly. Goaded not just by the taunts and teasing of the other children, but by her own natural avidity for learning, Alta became the outstanding student in her class with special talent in reading and writing. She was decidedly bookish but not unsociable. She had rarely missed the frequent dances at school, and now that she was living on her own and working, she was regularly included in socials around town. Her parents had, once again, moved to Cedaredge, where the lower elevation and warmer, less severe climate better suited their Mediterranean roots.

Alta had chosen to stay in Telluride. It was her home and she loved it. There was nowhere else on earth, she was convinced, even in Italy (despite her father's firm avowals to the contrary), that was as beautiful.

She was saddened that the town no longer flourished. As a girl growing up, Telluride had always been such an exciting place. There had always been something going on, day and night. She had vivid memories from when she first came back from Italy of Colorado Avenue being dense with the traffic of mule trains, occasional cars, and people on foot and on horseback. The Tomboy Road, which led from the top of Oak Street to the big mines in Marshall and Savage Basins — the Liberty Bell, Smuggler-Union, and the Tomboy — was never quiet. Even after the trams were built, stretching over miles of steep slopes and tying the high mines to the processing plant at the east end of the valley floor, the road still served as the main conduit to transport ore down to town and supplies of every kind back up into the mountains.

Telluride was a twenty-four-hour town when she had been growing up. From the train depot on the south side by the river, to the transfer station in the middle of town, to the smelter at the far east end of the box canyon and the trams that radiated in all directions from it like spokes on a wheel, the town had throbbed with constant industry. Now it seemed to be, if not all the way on its knees, at least in a prayerful pose.

Over the past several years, and at an accelerating rate, the mines had been winding down their operations, and more and more were terminating altogether. Prices were soft and costs were high. Before gold and silver had been discovered, there had been no Telluride. There had been nothing in the box canyon but the river that flowed from the end of it, tumbling more than three hundred feet down Bridal Veil Falls, and before the snows fell and after they melted, the Utes. Now, with the mines closing, it occurred to Alta that the valley might well revert again to an isolated and uninhabitable place. Everyone was feeling the pinch of the constricting economy and, almost daily of late, more and more people were deciding to move on in search of a brighter future.

Even the *Daily Journal*, where Alta worked part-time as assistant editor and author of a glorified busybody column called "People You Know," was surviving financially thanks only to the county legal notices and the cigarette companies' ads. Claude Trickett, who had come from Fruita in April as the paper's new editor and manager, had already determined, though it hadn't been publicly announced, that the *Journal* was going to have to convert from a daily to a weekly format in order to save money and avoid shutting down. Alta doubted that the announcement, when it did come, would cause much surprise or even disappointment. With things in town as they now were, there wasn't news enough to carry a daily anyway, and most of what news there was, was bad. Already the paper was relying heavily on national and international stories coming over the Western Union wire to fill its front page.

Alta felt lucky to have a second job as postmistress. The pay was not high, but it was reliable, and it kept her in close touch with just about everyone, which was good for keeping her column current on people's comings and goings. It pained her, though, that so many mailboxes were closed with no forwarding addresses and, in many cases, simply abandoned. About the only people who were able to keep afloat these days were certain of the bootleggers, of whom Telluride had more than a few. Telluride whiskey, so she understood, was renowned throughout the country and even in Canada. For a time, in the early days of Prohibition, which came several years earlier to Colorado than to the rest of the nation, a still was in operation by better than half the households in town. The alleys were deep then with discarded mash, and Alta, on her way to and from school, had more than occasionally made wide detours to avoid drunken chickens and ducks that feasted on the mash dregs and often became quite hostile.

Gambling, alcohol, and prostitution had always been a part of Telluride. In the years of booming prosperity, they had come to seem incidental. Now they had virtually become economic mainstays, and even they were on a steady decline. It was deeply troubling for Alta to imagine when the town's slide would end and what would become of it. So long as there was any town at all, and a need for a postmistress, she assumed she would stay.

Alta closed the book that had been resting unread in her lap while her mind wandered. She ran her long, tapered fingers through hair that she liked to describe as honey-colored but that was, in fact, predominantly red. She put the book down on the side table and got up from her chair to go to her bedroom window. It was a beautiful summer night. The moonlight shone on the spruce trees and their shadows were cast almost to the end of the block. It was quiet and still. She saw the lights go out in the Waggoner's house and two figures came down the front steps and into the moonlight. It was the banker and his wife.

Alta had known them almost her entire life. At one point, she had experienced a quite delicious crush on their son, Delos, who was a few years older than her. Waggoner, Sr., was a good and kind person, she thought. He was always at the ready to help those in need. He was a quiet man, almost apologetic in build, with a shy smile and a deferential attitude that she liked. As president of the only bank in town, he could have held himself above others and imposed his influence with a heavy hand. He never had.

Alta wondered what pressure Waggoner and the bank must be under with times turning as bad as they were. In the *Daily Journal*, the Bank of Telluride heralded itself in its ads as "a strong bank with capital and surplus of $100,000.00." And yet the news of small banks failing all over the state was increasingly common. She personally knew any number of people in town who were struggling to break even. If they had loans from the bank, which surely most did, it seemed unlikely they would be able to easily repay them, if at all. It occurred to Alta that every time she had been into the bank lately, Waggoner had been in closed-door meetings. His office had a large window, so that he could view the bank lobby. Through it, she had repeatedly seen him over the past several weeks at his desk, listening to customers on the other side, his brow creased, his thin lips pursed. She did not envy him. She imagined that being a banker in tough times must not be unlike a priest taking confession, the difference being that the banker's power resided only in gold, not God.

Waggoner and his wife got into their Studebaker, which Alta noticed had a full luggage rack. It was odd that they should be leaving town at such a late hour; odder still that she should know nothing about it.

The Studebaker coughed into ignition, its lights came on, and it began to move down the street. Alta stepped back from the window as the big car glided past beneath. The driver's side of the car was toward her and, as he drove past, Waggoner glanced up at her lighted window. Alta wasn't sure, but it seemed that he nodded to her and gave a sad half-smile.

CHAPTER TWO

Anise Koen awoke with a start. It was dark and quiet in her cell, the only light coming from a single dull bulb that hung by a bare cord perhaps fifteen feet down the hall. The only noise was the sound of snoring, errant murmurs, coughs, and sighs from other cells. Her bed was uncomfortable. The mattress was thin and old and seemed as if it were deliberately conspiring against her contours. Worst of all, the mattress smelled. Even through the harsh odor of the sheets, bleached with lye, she could detect the accumulated redolence of years of sweat and tears and the peculiar stench of fear that she had come to learn the body could produce, especially at night. Her mattress was soaked in the stale reek of it. Who knew how many prisoners had tossed and turned on this sickly mattress, bawled desperately into it, pleaded vainly with it to let them escape from their minds' torments by attaining just a few hours of uninterrupted sleep?

She cursed John Finnegan, the Delta sheriff. Until he had imposed himself, she had been given considerable freedom under Matron's supervision. She had had quite the run of the place before, to the point that it had scarcely felt like confinement at all but more of a convalescence. It had been like a not terribly exciting stay at a drab resort. Matron had spoiled her. Everyone had, really. They all thought her very glamorous and bright, nothing like the usual denizens of the Delta State Correctional Center. They had given her special food and treats, allowed her to stroll the grounds as often and as long as she liked, and, best of all, she had slept in a proper bed in a room with Matron that was left unlocked.

Then, one day the week before, the sheriff had come looking for her and could not find her. As it happened, she and Matron had left the penitentiary for the afternoon and had been in town doing nothing more sinister than visiting a beauty salon, taking tea, and admiring some new items of fashion at Delta's leading and only boutique. The sheriff had not been pleased. He had gone straight to Judge Bruce and complained that Anise had violated the trust reposed in her and taken advantage of the liberties allowed her.

Anise turned angrily in her bed, cursing the sheriff again and the defiant mattress. She cursed the Telluride bondsmen, too, who, after she was arrested and released on bail, had contrived to be excused from their commitments so that she was taken back into custody. When she had been appointed assistant county treasurer for San Miguel County, she had had trouble finding any bondsmen at all. If she had been a man, she thought, and preferably an older man and dull, there would have been no such problem. Instead, she was a beautiful young woman with brains and ambition, and the Telluride establishment characters that would normally have stepped up and offered surety were intimidated by her, she had concluded, and distrustful. If it hadn't been for the bank president, C.D. Waggoner, the bond might never have been raised at all. It was Waggoner who had persuaded the bondsmen to back her, in effect guarantying them against any loss. As the bank president, his guaranty, expressed or implied, was a good one and her appointment had been upheld.

Waggoner had been awfully good to her, and she had found it difficult not to be a bit flirtatious with him. He was twice her age, and, with his little round glasses, thin lips, and almost grotesquely big ears, he was hardly an object of attraction. Yet he had a quiet, self-effacing, old-fashioned charm, and he treated her with respect. He was also her last best chance to have her appointment ratified and approved, so she had not hesitated to use her feminine wiles, arranging herself in his office at the bank so that he could not help but see more than was strictly decorous, and leaning closely toward him so that the scent of her perfume and the very vitality of her skin could not go unnoticed.

She had been good at her job as assistant treasurer, extremely good. When Otto Brandes, the treasurer, fell ill, she had taken over his responsibilities without a qualm and carried them out better than ever he had himself. She smiled, remembering with irony how proud she had felt in the dark and despairing days immediately after her arrest to read Alta Cassietto's article in the paper where she was lauded as "the most capable young woman ever in the position of assistant county treasurer."

From a cell a few down from hers someone spoke out in their sleep, a mumbled cryptic string of nonsense. Anise turned on to her stomach and squeezed her eyes against the tears she could not stop. The mattress, underneath the bleached sheets, readily soaked them in.

The following day, Walter Hillman came to visit Anise. Hillman was the vice president and cashier of the Delta National Bank. He had been to Telluride on bank business in the past and had met Anise, so he said, but she honestly could not recall. It was nice to have a visitor, however, and she pretended that she remembered the meeting with perfect clarity. Hillman was in his early thirties, tall, and attractive in a not terribly original way. Without a jacket and tie, she imagined him to look like any number of the cowboys whom she had so often sensed casting their lupine glances at her as she walked down Colorado Avenue.

Hillman had an air of earnestness that Anise quickly came to find rather unsettling. She would have preferred her caller to be of a lighter disposition to help lift her from the dark funk into which she had found herself settling deeper and deeper as the day of her sentencing drew nearer. She would have liked a visitor who could distract her with rapid idle chatter, a conversationalist, someone who could, at least for the brief time that they were together, help her to forget what she had done, where she was, and what was likely to be her fate. Hillman seemed incapable of any of that. If anything, he was making her feel worse by his edgy reserve and awkward manner.

Why he had come she wasn't sure. He had not been able to clearly articulate his motives. He had stammered through an explanation, how he had been following her story and how badly he felt for her and what pressured times these were. In fact, it had been such an unsatisfactory explanation that Anise would have feigned a headache or complained with some other excuse to cut the meeting short but for two things. The first was that there was entirely absent in Hillman's stumbling words any hint of judgment. The second was that she was genuinely lonely. Apart from Matron, whose company could be best compared to a pet dog's, the only other visitations that Anise had enjoyed, or endured, depending on the moment, had been her mother's, who spent the majority of their time together either hugging her too tightly or weeping disconsolately, or both. Hillman, as short of charm as he might be, was at least doing neither of those two things. And, however difficult it was for him to express it, Anise readily sensed that his character ran well deeper than Matron's. As much as she would have preferred not to have to, Anise made the effort to keep the conversation detoured around the cul-de-sacs and roadblocks toward which her visitor was prone to steer it.

"What is it that you do when you're not toiling slavishly at the bank, Mr. Hillman? Have you family here in Delta? Do you read extensively? What are your tastes in literature? Do you prefer fiction or fact? What character from a novel could you imagine yourself to be? Describe for me what a perfect day's outing would be for you."

Hillman answered her questions dutifully but without flourish. Small talk was not easy for him, it was more and more apparent. Anise pressed on, nonetheless, preferring unsatisfactory small talk to none at all. She set herself to ply him with additional interrogation when he suddenly reached out and caught her arm, squeezing it. In his eyes shone a light of fear that perfectly matched the feeling that she fought so vigilantly against in herself. Whatever vapid words she had been about to utter were silenced. Hillman, however, had no words of his own to take their place.

"What is it, Mr. Hillman? Whatever is it that you want? I'm afraid you are making me quite nervous and uncomfortable."

He withdrew his hand and used it to rub his brow worriedly, then covered his eyes. Then he uncovered them and Anise noticed how tired he suddenly seemed. In his eyes, mixed with the look of fear, was exhaustion.

"Why did you do it?" Hillman asked. The look in his eyes had changed yet again and was now plaintive, like a little boy's, as if he needed and expected a short, simple answer that could neatly tidy up a mess that he was making in his own mind.

Anise was taken aback. She had certainly not expected the question and she had no easy answer to it. She had needed the money, of course, but that wasn't the full explanation, by any means. She could have borrowed the money, at least part of it, most of it; and she could have scrimped and saved and done without in order to continue to get by. Anise had not yet, herself, clearly, completely, reasoned through her act. She had, frankly, devoted more time to considering what she could have done differently to avoid being caught than she had questioning why she had done it in the first place.

"I don't know," she answered hesitantly. "Why does anyone do anything they shouldn't? Why do people take advantage of each other? Why is there cheating, lying, fighting? I don't know the answer, Mr. Hillman. If it pleases you, I can weave a nice fairy tale that will cast me in a most favorable light and that will allow you to see me as no more than a victim of injustice and hypocrisy. Is that what you would like me to do?"

Hillman closed his eyes and shook his head and looked almost as if he would cry.

Anise's tone had been stinging and she regretted it. It was not wrong of her visitor to ask her what he had, however much of a stranger he might be. It was simply unexpected and painfully direct. She reached out her hand and touched his.

"What *is* the matter, Mr. Hillman? You are evidently deeply troubled and have come to me with the idea that I might somehow be of help. What is it that's troubling you? Do tell me."

Oddly, by opening up to her caller, by putting herself at his service, as it were, she felt the yoke of her own troubles loosen and lift, though only a little. She pressed his hand.

"Tell me," she urged.

Hillman looked at her and, again, shook his head. He stood up, pulling his hand from under hers.

"I have to go," he said.

Anise did not respond and he stood awkwardly fumbling with his hat. "May I come again?"

She smiled. "You may," she answered. "But you had better not wait too long. My trial is in just three days. After that I may be sent somewhere rather less convenient." She gave a short laugh, but there was no gaiety in it. Hillman responded with a grim smile, then turned and left. For several minutes Anise sat and stared at the chair where he had sat. Then she, too, got up and left the visiting room.

CHAPTER THREE

Driving at night in the mountains was perilous. The road was rough and serpentine and dotted by rocks that had loosened and rolled from above, some of them large enough to do serious damage; even the small ones were a hazard. As often as not, the roadbed fell away precipitously to one side or the other, a yawning abyss waiting to pull an unwary driver to a horrendous end. Waggoner was familiar with the highway and he welcomed its desertion at night: no need to speed up, slow down, pass, and be passed at the whim of other drivers. Still, he couldn't relax his attention for a moment. The moonlight helped, but there were still shadows and darkened bends where no light penetrated save the Studebaker's headlights. Twice, Waggoner had been forced to brake strenuously to avoid hitting small herds of elk moving across the roadway. Once, he thought he glimpsed a mountain lion crouched atop a ledge that jutted out above the road, but he couldn't be sure. He had, by then, been driving for several hours, and his eyes were no longer entirely trustworthy. He knew he should stop and sleep, as Mary had urged him to several times before she herself had drifted into slumber beside him. As long as he could keep his eyes open, however, Waggoner meant to keep going. He hoped to reach Denver before nightfall the next day, and the following day to set out for Olathe, near Kansas City, where his sister lived. It was an aggressive goal but not impossible. While he drove, he plied himself with coffee from a thermos.

The Waggoners' son, Delos, was in Denver paying a visit to his fiancée. Although Waggoner had been unable, unprepared, to explain the reasons fully to Mary, she knew that they would not be able to be in touch with their son while they were there. "Please trust me," Waggoner had told his wife. "What he doesn't know can't hurt him." The same applied to Mary, but he had felt no need to say so to her.

In fact, ever since Delos had come to work at the bank with his father, he had been kept largely in the dark. He complained regularly that he hadn't enough to do or responsibility enough. The tone of Waggoner's response was always the same.

"No need to rush things," he counseled. "Business is slow. Take advantage of the time now to learn all you can about the basic business of the bank. The better you understand the nuts and bolts, the better you'll be able to run the bank when the day comes."

Delos was increasingly less mollified by such words, Waggoner knew. It didn't help that the loan side of the bank was what most interested his son, and that Scanlon and he kept everything to do with that critical part of the bank's business under close wraps.

Certainly his son's tutelage was far different from what his uncle had given him. James Brown had been a founder of the bank and had served for several years as its president. At his sister's request, he had invited his nephew to come West and take a job at the bank.

"The essential business of banking," Brown had explained on his nephew's first day, "is an eminently simple one. Money is taken from depositors who haven't immediate need of it, or all of it, and it's loaned out to borrowers who need more than they have. The difference between the interest the bank pays to the depositors for the use of their funds and that paid by the borrowers on their loans is the main source of the bank's income." The "interest margin," James Brown had called it.

"Charge enough interest," he had once told his nephew, "make your margin ample enough and, in theory at least, over the long-term, it becomes secondary whether or not you are ever paid back the principal you first loaned." That said, he schooled his scion rigorously in ways to make sure the principal was paid back, on time and in full.

"It's loans that make the bank its profit," he stressed. "You pay out the least you can to the depositors to attract their savings, pennies on the dollar, and you charge your debtors the most that they can bear to pay. The more risk in the loan defaulting, the higher an interest rate you stipulate. And never make a loan that has but one source of repayment, for there is always the possibility, and often the probability, that something unforeseen will transpire to compromise that source. Or eradicate it entirely. The market rate for cattle may fall and leave a rancher short. Or his herd may suffer disease. The extra business counted on by a merchant by expanding his line of products may be negated by a new competitor opening shop. A crop of hay or wheat may be ruined by drought or flooding. Expect the worst, always, and prepare against it. Secure yourself with pledged assets of hard value, surety of any and every available kind: guaranties, assignments of insurances, assignments of rights and contracts, land, a house, stocks and bonds, jewelry — whatever the borrower owns that the bank can control and liquidate if it has to.

"Never forget," he exhorted his nephew, "that the time, effort, and cost to recover a bad loan can easily strip the bank of profit made on half-a-dozen good ones of equal face value."

And then there had been the issue of fees. About these, James Brown was equally emphatic.

"Nothing is free!" he declared. "Nor should it be. Yes, we pay our depositors for giving us their money, but we charge them, too. As guardians of their money, we perform a valuable service. It is only right and proper that they should pay us for that. And the beauty is," he went on, a glint of cold delight in his eyes, "we send no bill for payment. We do not invoice the customer and wait to be paid, or not. We take the fees, in advance, directly from the customer's account. Monthly statements? Two dollars. Reconciliation of transactions? One dollar. One dollar fifty to negotiate a bill or issue a draft. Sending monies and receiving monies, fees to both parties, taken directly from the monies concerned."

There were fees to be assessed on loans, as well. Unlike the interest charge, gauged according to the loan's risk, its likelihood of being repaid as agreed, the assessed fees were to cover the amount of work involved in putting the loan in place. Simple loans, short-term accommodations to bridge a temporary timing difference in the borrower's stream of payments and receipts, were charged lesser fees. Longer-term mortgages, chattel loans to ranchers, loans involving multiple parties or complicated by the nature of the collateral securing them, came with higher fees. Again, these were not billed to the borrower for payment but assessed and taken in advance.

"If the borrower needs the full value of the borrowed funds," Waggoner's uncle counseled him, "add the fee to the amount of the loan and pay it back to the bank immediately, as soon as monies are disbursed to the borrower. Otherwise, net the fee from the monies advanced. And no fee should be negotiable. You may have to bicker and dance with a borrower about terms of repayment, about the interest rate, about guaranties, or collateral or insurance or whatever it may be. But you should never equivocate on fees. You establish what you require to comfortably cover your costs, including your personal time and your staff's, and you stick with that, even at the risk of the customer taking his business elsewhere. No fee should ever come to be seen as arbitrary or unnecessary. But, of course, you have to deliver value. No one minds paying for value. No one you would ever want as a customer, at any rate. Indeed, I have found it true repeatedly that customers will only too gladly pay premiums for services well-delivered. And the more cut and dry you are about the fee, the more adamantine your posture, the more palatable it is to them. If a banker is prepared to quibble over a fee, he makes it seem a vague and perhaps dispensable component of the transaction. If, instead, the matter of the fee is presented with the same incontrovertibility of a judge's ruling, none will question it."

More than anything else that his uncle taught him about his trade, two tenets had remained forever embedded in Waggoner's memory. The first was to do with fraud.

"If a man means to defraud the bank," Brown had advised, "if he sets out with a will and purpose to deliberately defalcate, your chances of recovering your funds are few, indeed. Once money goes out the door, it is always at risk of never coming back. Just so, a skilled perpetrator, no matter how well you think you may have defended yourself against a loss, will best you if that is his intent. That's just the way it is."

The second tenet led directly from the first.

"Regardless of how well you do your job as a lender," his uncle cautioned, "despite how well you have thought a loan through, secured it as best you can, wrapped it like a Christmas package in legal papers, don't ever close it, don't ever put your name to it or authorize the bank to disburse it, if you don't feel secure in your own gut. If a bad feeling nags you, there's a reason. A banker can apply all the science he cares to, he can analyze and second-guess and require a hundred pages of agreements and signatures. But, if his instinct isn't at ease, he needs to pay attention to it — as much attention or more as he pays to anything the borrower tells him or the borrower's lawyer or the borrower's best friend or his business associates tell him. Bad loans don't become bad with time. They become worse. Time serves merely to allow you to fully recognize them for what they were in the first place, and by then it's too late. Then your loan papers be damned. You'd be as well off with a daguerreotype of a handshake. By the time you know the true state of things, your borrower will have already, whether honestly or dishonestly, dug a hole for you that you won't get out of without a lot of sweat and even more luck. If you do manage to get out, you'll find you've a quantity of gray hairs you never had before and new wrinkles on your face that haven't come from the sun or too many smiles."

As well as Waggoner had understood his uncle's counsel, as much sense as it made, he had to admit that it never came to him easily to follow his instincts. Not absolutely, at least. And it wasn't that he didn't notice or recognize them. He did. He could virtually tell within minutes how a loan request felt to him in his gut. But there were so many other factors to consider. Things were not as black and white for him as they were for his uncle. They were shaded, gray and tenuous. He was not the success his uncle was and had not the same confidence of success. He had not, as James Brown had, built a fortune and a sterling reputation for himself. He had nothing like his uncle's stern and strict character either, nothing of his strong will or the cold acumen of his business savvy. Where his uncle, if he thought it necessary or prudent, could say "no" to anyone, regardless of their name or stature or their need, Waggoner found that he could not. He was easily drawn in to the stories his customers and prospective customers shared with him, their plights and predicaments, their schemes. Where his uncle's first thought was of the bank, of making the best possible return for its shareholders, of safeguarding them against loss, Waggoner's was often not. He found that frequently his first inclination was to help the person on the other side of his desk, to make things work for them, to facilitate the request that they had brought to him.

To say "no" was something he found fundamentally difficult. No one wanted to hear "no." There was no joy in that word. Acquaintances could sour, friendships could dissolve over the word. With "no" could come unseemly pleadings, insults, threats, even tears. And the people he would have to say "no" to were the people he lived among. They were the people he passed on the street, stood in line behind at the grocer's, knelt beside at church to pray. He was not a combative person. He took no joy in opposition or ill will. His uncle, on the other hand, seemed to care nothing of what people thought of him, good or bad. He had staunch and unshakeable convictions about things and a steadfast sense of identity that Waggoner had never quite found in himself.

The Studebaker passed through Gunnison and beside the long, level plain of the Gunnison River. It was past four in the morning. Mary had awakened once, but had fallen back to sleep. Though his body was tired, Waggoner's mind was activated by the coffee. A mist hung above the river and spread in patches across the highway, some of them dense enough to be blinding. The Studebaker's lights only made it worse, as the beams were caught by the fog and then refracted. It was alarming to have the car speed into a drift of cloud and suddenly see nothing ahead but haloed light. Some of the mist clouds seemed to hold the car for minutes, though Waggoner knew it was only seconds. He slowed the car until the road began to climb out of the valley and the mist was left behind. Within a few miles, the first winding bends began that would describe the rest of the drive up and over Monarch Pass. Waggoner allowed himself to relax again as he gave the Studebaker more gas. His thoughts returned to his early years in Telluride, working at the bank. Owing to his uncle's influence, he had moved ahead quickly. Far more quickly, he always felt, than he could ever otherwise have advanced. Far more quickly, he admitted to himself, than he deserved on sheer merit.

Within three years, his uncle had largely removed himself from his position at the bank. Within five, he had relinquished all responsibility and retained merely an ownership interest. The presidency was managed for an interim of two years by Oliver Frye, who had served with Brown as vice president and cashier since the bank's inception. Then Frye had stepped down, and the reins were handed to Waggoner. The promotion to president was welcomed, but Waggoner had not felt confident of his abilities. And times in Telluride, though still robust, were changing, becoming harder. Clashes between the miners and the owners were still not irregular, and the animosity between them, and between their empathizers, was palpable and constant. Both sides did business with the bank. Waggoner's customers were as likely to be one as the other. The side of the owners represented the town's wealth, or control of the wealth, but the miners represented many more actual customers. And though their individual loans and deposits were immaterial in comparison to the accounts of the owners and their constituents, they were, in total, hardly insignificant. The Miners' Union itself was actually becoming one of the bank's larger accounts. And there were union sympathizers who were shopkeepers and saloon owners and professionals — doctors, lawyers, surveyors — who were all bank customers.

Apart from the divided loyalties that he felt were imposed on him by his position, Waggoner honestly didn't know where his true sympathies lay. He could never have admitted that to his friend Bulkeley Wells, let alone suggest, as he would have had to if he were to be completely honest, that he sympathized more closely with the demands of the miners than he did the edicts of the owners.

A chuckle escaped Waggoner as he imagined Wells' probable response if he had ever dared reveal his feelings to him. His wife stirred at the noise, and it occurred to Waggoner that he hadn't laughed aloud for a long time.

"Fuck, Buck," Wells would have said. Almost the only time Waggoner ever heard his friend say this was when they were alone together and Wells had taken a drink or two. It was nothing more than a two-word expostulation, of which the second was his nickname and the first a rhyming expletive. Wells had never really taken to calling him Buck, although the rest of Telluride had quite universally. Perhaps it was because Wells and he first met before the name had been conferred on him. Waggoner would never forget that meeting. It was in the very early days of both their arrivals from the East. His uncle had held a large dinner party in honor of some visiting financiers from New York. It was a formal and lavish affair, his uncle's house at the top of North Oak Street festooned with fresh flowers and more Waterford crystal and Limoges china than Waggoner had ever seen. The party was catered by the Japanese chef from the Sheridan named Weh, and beautiful Japanese girls with long, silken, jet hair moved like silent smiling dolls among the guests, serving hors d'oeuvres and drinks and, later, dinner that consisted of six different courses. Apart from James Brown's fiancée, Mary Reade, Wells and Waggoner were by far the youngest guests. But that was where any similarity between them seemed to end. Waggoner, not an outgoing person by nature, felt even more than usually reticent surrounded by so many sophisticates. He sipped his drink and fidgeted in the jacket pocket of the new tailored suit his uncle had bought him, the fabric for which Mary had helped him choose, chiding him playfully at the time for debating between one he really liked and one that was not as nice but far less expensive. It was the first tailored suit he had ever owned, and, as perfectly as it fit, he felt awkward in it, as if he didn't belong in anything so fine. Unlike the other guests who seemed as if they might have been born in their finery, the women all in wasp-waisted, bustled silk gowns and the men in starched white shirts with high collars, Waggoner felt like an imposter in his new fancy clothes. If anything, they made him more self-conscious than ever.

Wells had arrived at the party a little late, but not unfashionably so. As Waggoner came to know him later, he realized that it was a typical ploy of Wells' to ensure that he could not help but become the center of attention at any gathering. This should hardly have been a consideration, in Waggoner's opinion. Wells was such a commanding figure with his tall, erect bearing, perfect manners, and consummate charm that he attracted attention naturally. He was also the most handsome man that Waggoner had ever seen. His dark hair was full and sleek with expensive oil that made it shine, and his eyes — beneath brows that could have been penciled on by an artist, they were so perfect and perfectly matched — were as full and dark and shining as his hair. He was extravagantly handsome, saved from prettiness by a just heavy enough jaw and a slight crook to his smile.

Wells strode into the roomful of chatter and clinking glasses with complete self-containment, his eyes alive with the scene that he beheld, a scene with which he was obviously as at ease as Waggoner was discomfited. He nodded genially at small groups of men that he recognized but went immediately to Mary Reade, who stood with a clutch of other women, all of them, in Waggoner's eyes, bedecked like princesses, their long hair coiffed and curled in pendant ringlets, their bracelets and necklaces flashing brightly with every gesture. They turned to greet Wells, who took each of their proffered hands in turn and lifted them to bestow a chaste kiss. The same hands had been offered Waggoner earlier, and the thought of kissing them had not even remotely occurred to him. He had, instead, shaken them, and with none of Wells' gentility.

Wells accepted Mary Reade's hand last and took it in both his, then leaned toward her and kissed her with the same certain grace as he had the other ladies' hands — once on each cheek in the Continental fashion. She turned her face to accommodate him with a practiced ease.

What words Wells spoke Waggoner did not hear, but it was evidently something suitably gay, for the women all smiled delightedly on hearing them. Then Mary took him by the arm and, much to the apparent disappointment of the other ladies, led him away, directly toward the corner of the room where Waggoner had been quietly studying the party's rising merriment. For a moment, he felt as if he would feign need of a drink or an hors d'oeuvre and try to disappear into another room. Wells was all that he felt he was not, and he had no enthusiasm to have that feeling confirmed by a formal introduction.

As it happened, he had no need to worry. Wells was completely relaxed in the introduction and exhibited none of the hauteur or disinterest that Waggoner had feared and expected.

"So," offered Wells when Mary Reade had left them to attend to other guests. "You're new to town, Charles? That makes us two of a kind. I arrived only a few weeks ago. Stunning place. I don't think I've ever seen anywhere quite so beautiful. Have you?"

"No," said Waggoner. "No, I don't believe I have." He hesitated, trying vainly to think of something that Wells might consider clever or witty or simply intelligent. He searched for the right adjective to describe Telluride, but in vain.

"It's very...beautiful."

Wells laughed and nodded appreciatively, as if he thought Waggoner's words the perfect ones, culled adroitly from the vast universe of the English language. Waggoner relaxed immediately and laughed as well.

"Yes," he went on, emboldened, but his tongue had not yet shed its shyness, and he found he had no idea what he might have intended to add. Wells looked at him expectantly, his face still creased by his crooked smile, his dark eyes still twinkling with mirth. Waggoner felt himself flushing, a feeling of terrible inadequacy rushing back, and no words surfaced to save him.

"Very beautiful," he stammered at last.

Wells' laugh this time was loud enough and jolly enough that several people turned, smiling their way to see if they might share in the amusement. Wells seemed not to notice and kept his attention fully on Waggoner. As if they were old friends, he clasped the smaller man on the shoulder.

"You've obviously a taste for poetry, Mr. Waggoner," he said without a hint of derision. "I suggest we take seats next to one another for dinner. I expect a great friendship to develop between us, and I think it should start in all earnestness this very evening. What do you say?"

Waggoner's smile lacked something of Wells' effusion but, for him, it was a wide one.

"I should think that would be splendid," he answered, trying to achieve a note of Wells' rich tone and cadence. Then they had both laughed together, and Wells swept him from his isolated corner to fetch a fresh drink and immerse themselves in the festive ambience.

✵ ✵ ✵

The coffee from Waggoner's thermos was nearly gone. The quantity he had already consumed now swelled his bladder. Halfway up the ascent to Monarch Pass, he pulled the Studebaker to the side of the road and got out to relieve himself. The moon had moved across the night sky, and dawn was perhaps just an hour away. Waggoner felt satisfied with their progress. He had fueled the Studebaker in Montrose and had gas enough in the automobile's tank to get over the mountain. He would burn less going down the other side. By the time they reached Salida, there would be somewhere to buy more and to get breakfast.

The quiet of the night was deep and clear, the air pungent of pine and sage. Waggoner breathed it in. He would have liked to stretch his legs, to find a rancher's track or an elk path and pad quietly along it into the moon-shadowed cover of the mountain's forest. Instead he squatted into a short series of knee bends and then got back into the Studebaker. Mary stirred and woke. She smiled at her husband and then fussed a moment with her hair that had been pressed flat against the side of her head by the back of her seat.

"G'morning," she mumbled. "Where are we?"

"Halfway up to the pass. It's just four o'clock. You should sleep some more."

"What of you?" she asked. "Why not let me drive?"

She knew his answer in advance. Her husband was a good and careful driver, but he was the very model of a bad passenger, prone to giving unasked-for advice to the driver and clearly uncomfortable at not having control of the steering wheel and the foot pedals.

"It's okay. I'm fine. I still have some coffee left. Perhaps we can switch after breakfast. It'll just be an hour or so."

Mary nodded without argument.

"You're okay?" she asked.

Waggoner knew she was no longer asking about his physical state, his ability to stay awake and continue driving. He had not explicitly detailed for her the urgency of their departure. He had told her merely that the bank was in trouble and that he knew of only one way to save it. He patted her arm. How many other wives, he wondered, would on such short and unsatisfactory notice prepare for a journey of unknown duration and set out upon it under cover of night and voice not a word of complaint?

"I'm fine," he smiled. "Go back to sleep. Next stop, eggs and bacon."

Mary smiled back and closed her eyes. Waggoner couldn't help but discern a crease of worry between her brows.

He started the car again and steered it back on to the road, taking another gulp of coffee as he did. His thoughts turned quickly back to the past, to the dinner party at his uncle's, to the evening when Telluride first began to reveal itself to him fully.

Good to his word, Wells had come looking for him when the dinner bell was sounded.

"Come, Charles," he urged, his arm around the other's shoulder as if they were old Harvard classmates rather than the most recent acquaintances. "Your uncle's fiancée deemed it appropriate to place name cards at the tables. I noticed that she had in the hectic activities of her other preparations made an oversight or two in their placement. I'm certain she will thank me for taking the liberty of one or two slight rearrangements."

Waggoner's uncle's large formal table had been removed from the dining room and replaced by half-a-dozen smaller round ones, each of them set for parties of six. The tables were covered in beige damask and, to Waggoner's eyes, a bewildering array of silver cutlery and crystal glasses of varying dimensions. As Wells had said, there were place cards at each setting. Beside the seat reserved for Wells was one with Waggoner's card.

As they stood waiting for the rest of the party to enter the room and for the ladies to be seated, Wells whispered to him conspiratorially. "I'm afraid there were some other adjustments required," he said. "Miss Reade had chosen one or two of her other guests for this table who I knew would have been happier elsewhere. So I helped them by placing them at more appropriate tables." He feigned a yawn to indicate that the formerly designated occupants were not suitably jolly or engaging.

Waggoner wondered if Mary Reade would notice and, if so, what she might say or do. Wells showed no such concern. He greeted the rest of their table as they arrived as if he couldn't believe the luck of his draw. Besides Waggoner, there was his uncle, Frank Brown, James's older brother, and his wife Henrietta, and Mr. and Mrs. Otto Mears. He never knew who had been replaced. And if Mary Reade noticed, she showed no sign of perturbation. Nor need she have. The dinner party was an unqualified success. The food was quite literally the best Waggoner had ever tasted, flavored with an array of intoxicating herbs and sauces. The wines were all French and, so Wells told him, of excellent vintage. He wouldn't have known. His taste ran to sarsaparilla and an occasional ginger beer. He knew, though, that the wines were delicious and that they were contributing generously to the party's festive mood. Not that encouragement was required. Between the many toasts proposed, the limitless food, and the ever-rising hubbub of conversation, every table was engrossed in enjoyment and no one looked to be the odd-one-out.

He had expected Wells to hold court at their table, but that was not the case. His new friend was very much a part of the conversation and conviviality, but he in no way led or dominated it. He might not have been able to even had he wanted. Between Mears and Waggoner's uncle, and their respective tales of the old days, true or tall, there was little room for interjection. Wells seemed to mind not in the least and was the first to prompt another story from the pair.

"They tell me that you were a friend of Geronimo's, Mr. Brown," he said to Waggoner's uncle, a look of unbridled fascination in his eyes. "Is that true?"

Frank Brown was, in most respects, a complete contrast to his brother, James. Where the younger brother was tall and elegant, his air urbane, his manner touching on aloof, Frank was more compactly and powerfully built, with the rugged countenance and open mannerisms of a man more comfortable with a fence post than a pencil and with wearing a bandana rather than a tie or cravat. In his youth, he had been a drover for the Hayden Expedition that had first mapped the Southwest for the United States government. He had lived in Telluride since well before the town had been incorporated; his ranch house outside of town was one of the first built at the original mining camp location, before the early settlement moved east towards the canyon's end and was named Columbia and then, later, Telluride.

"Was and is and ever shall be a friend," he answered Wells, his voice deep with resonance and delivered with a cowboy drawl. "Best man I've ever known."

Waggoner's mouth dropped open. What he knew of Geronimo had been gleaned solely from newspaper accounts and frontier novels, depictions of the Apache leader that cast him as a merciless renegade bent on extermination of Whites: men, women, and children. His uncle's words were the equivalent, to his mind, of a Catholic paying homage to Satan.

No one else seemed to share his surprise, familiar perhaps with the story or simply with his uncle's penchant for shaking people from complacency. Waggoner glanced at Wells but saw nothing in his expression but rapt attention. Wells urged Brown to go on, and Otto Mears encouraged him as well.

"Tell zem ze story, Frank," he enthused, his accent still Russian, though he had immigrated to America as an orphan at fourteen and was now well into his fifties.

Brown showed no reluctance. "We were in the desert," he began. "I was out early, scouting while camp broke, trying to get vantage of high ground. It was desolate country, fiercer even than usual, nothing but rock and sand, tumbleweed and cacti. I found an arroyo cut by spring rains and followed it, the silt wash being easier on my horse. There was wind blowing at me, which is why I was able to come up on Geronimo the way I did. Otherwise he would have heard me, or more likely, smelled me. I came around a bend in the creek bed and there he was. His horse had pulled up lame, it seemed, and he was hunkered over, taking a look at its hoof. He was a smallish fella and unarmed, save for a knife and a quiver of arrows for his bow. I had two Colts and a Remington, so I wasn't worried. He looked a peaceable-enough type anyway, and, as I say, nothing big or strapping about him. Some braves I've seen would have put me in the mind of turning back and going the way I came, but I didn't have that feeling with this one. His horse was one of the finer I'd ever seen, too. So, I called to him in Shoshone.

"I reckoned he might be a little riled at being come up on unexpected by a paleface, but he wasn't. In fact, he didn't even stand, let alone run or grab for his steel or his bow. If I didn't know better, I'd have thought he was waiting on me to get there.

"I reined my horse right up to him and slipped off. I told him I was come in peace and that I was good at fixin' hurt horses.

"He told me his horse was young and had spooked at a rattlesnake and cut its hoof on a rock. He said he killed the rattler and ate it, but that the hoof-cut was deep and he couldn't seem to do much for it. I squatted and took a look. It was deep enough, all right. I gathered up some tumbleweed and dead cactus and such for a fire, put my canteen in it to heat some water, then cut a piece of leather off my saddlebag and a strip of rawhide from my reins. When the water was hot, I told him to keep a good hold on his horse, then I poured some of the water on its hoof. The horse wasn't too pleased with me, but Geronimo talked to it steady and low, and it didn't act up as much as I thought it might. Then I soaked my bandana in the hot water, tied it around the hoof, and then tied the leather over that like a boot.

"It didn't fix the horse for riding, but it could walk again, at least. I offered to ride the Indian back on my horse wherever he was going and lead his horse behind. He allowed that that would be fine, that he was meeting a party of his people not far from where we were. I thought of asking him for his knife, as I didn't cotton to the idea of it getting poked between my ribs as we rode, but somehow I seemed to know that wasn't going to happen.

"Once we were riding, he told me his name was Goyathlay. That means 'the one who yawns.' Of course, at the time it didn't mean a thing to me, as this was before his long campaign against being removed from his ancestor lands, before he came to be known as the greatest-ever Chiricahua warrior. He didn't even have the name Geronimo yet. That was given to him later by the Mexicans, at the time when the legends of his powers came to be known. It was said that he could walk on sand and leave no prints, could turn himself invisible, and that no bullet could harm him. I don't know about the first two, but it's true enough that he fought thousands of American and Mexican soldiers alike without ever being wounded by a single bullet.

"While we rode, he chatted away. He told me he was born on the prairie, where the wind blew free and there was nothing to break the light of the sun. That he was born where there were no enclosures, and that he was warmed by the sun, rocked by the winds, and sheltered by the trees as other Indian babes were. He asked me if I thought a man's life was in vain, and he told me that he could not think that men were useless or God would not have created us. There is one God, he allowed, looking down on us all. We are all the children of one God, Indians the same as Whites. He said the sun, the darkness, and the winds all listen to what we have to say, no matter what our color.

"The way he talked, I came to know that he wasn't an average buck. And when we met up with his party, I heard him called by words that signified that he was a seer and a medicine man, a leader of his people, although not a chief.

"Though I didn't know it at the time, and perhaps just as well, the man who rode behind me on my horse was a man who could have happily killed me and felt every right to do so. In '58, not so many years before I met him, he came back from a trading run to Mexico to find that Spanish troops had murdered his wife, his mother, and his three young children."

Waggoner's food had suddenly gone cold and tasteless in his mouth at his uncle's words. The pain in Frank Brown's eyes for the two women and three children, whom he had never known, Waggoner felt, as well. There were people, many of them, for whom the name Geronimo was synonymous with blood-thirst and savagery. There was never a story he had read, in book or newspaper, that had made the Apache out as anything but the very embodiment of deviltry. No writer that he had ever read made even a single mention of the murder of his family, of what it would do to a man, any man, to return home from a time away to find that the people most dear to him were all dead, killed by other men with wives and mothers and children.

❀ ❀ ❀

From Monarch Pass, Waggoner could see first light beginning to break to the east. Another hour and it would be full daylight. With it would come traffic, although not much. The only towns for most of the way to Denver were small ones, located long distances apart from each other. Waggoner realized he would not be able to drive the whole way without stopping to sleep. He considered letting his wife drive and decided he would have to. She was not a bad driver — slow, overly cautious — but that was preferable to being a madwoman behind the wheel. He was not comfortable in a car if he wasn't in control. It would be nice, he mused, to be able to stop in Fairplay at a hotel and sleep properly on a bed, in fresh sheets, but that was impossible. They had to push on. Timing was critical, and the schedule he had set himself was tight. It allowed no delay. He let the Studebaker coast down the other side of the pass, risking the wear on its brakes for the sake of the gasoline in its tank.

❀ ❀ ❀

His uncle had stopped speaking after telling of the surprise given to his Indian friend by the Spanish troops. No one at the table seemed comfortable to break the silence, and it was Waggoner himself who finally did. "Did you see him again?"

"Oh, indeed," replied Brown. "I saw him two or three times over those several weeks as we did our survey work of that sector. We ended up doing some trading, horses and food and blankets. The deals were always square, neither Reds nor Whites getting or taking unfair advantage. He and I went hunting together, passed on what we knew and believed to each other, stood together on buttes at sunset saying nothing, just watching the desert change from day to night. I tell you, he may never have lived in a house, seen a commode, or eaten with a fork, but he was as civilized a man as I've ever known.

"And then, over the years, I would have word of him. I'd be somewhere, at a trading post maybe in Albuquerque or Santa Fe, and I'd meet an Indian that knew an Indian that knew Geronimo, and I'd ask them to send my regards and, sure enough, a month later or a year, I'd have word back. And then one night, perhaps it was '83 or so, during the time that he was on the lam from the U.S. and Mexican armies both, and no one could catch better than a glimpse of him disappearing, let alone kill him, he turned up at my door right here in Telluride. Don't ask me how he tracked me down, but he surely did. He knocked at the door as if he were a neighbor coming to borrow sugar for a cake. Henrietta opened it and near breathed her last at the sight of him, she was that shocked."

Waggoner's aunt smiled and nodded her head in agreement. "I would have screamed," she said, "but I had no voice. And no legs to run. If Frank hadn't come, I believe I might be standing there still, my eyes bulging and my mouth as wide open as the door."

"I was just in the other room," Frank went on. "I'd heard the knock and heard Henrietta open the door. Then, when I heard nothing more, I got up to see who was calling on us. You could have knocked me over with a feather when I did. Turns out the soldiers had chased him farther and farther north, all the way up past Cortez and toward Dolores. With so few of us living hereabouts in those days, my name was pretty familiar in both those areas, and somehow he found out about me and came to see if he could hide out awhile. Told me he didn't think it would occur to the soldiers to look for him in a White man's home." Brown chuckled. "He was right enough about that. We ended up having him as our guest for better'n a fortnight, time enough for the army to run itself ragged looking for him where he'd last been seen. Then one morning we woke up and he was gone. We never saw him again."

"Left without a word?" asked Wells. "That seems not so civilized."

"Well, I guess he wasn't much on goodbyes," Brown conceded. "But, then, he wasn't one to say hello, either. From the first time I met him in that arroyo, he just started in or left out talking as if before and after were not considerations for him. What would be and what had been all seemed to run together with what is for him, if you savvy. To show up out of nowhere and then be gone the same was the way he was. He told me once that if you met a person and got to know them, whether you liked them or not, then that person became alive in you, that you became connected by a force that was always with you. That person becomes part of who you are and you become a part of them. When you believe such a thing as that, I expect it isn't so important to present yourself or take your leave with words."

"No, I suppose it isn't," said Wells. "It's an interesting philosophy. I think I may adopt it as my own. It seems it would be a fine way to excuse myself my deficiencies. I could simply blame the people I know for making me the way I am."

"Yes," said Otto Mears. "But zen you vould 'ave ze problem zat zey, too, vould blame you for who zey are."

"And that, Mr. Mears," riposted Wells, "would be their kettle of fish, not mine."

"But, for Geronimo," Mears replied, "it seems all fish are in ze same kettle, no?"

Wells laughed delightedly. "Quite right. Touché. Rather difficult to be the fish that got away in such a world. Perhaps I shan't adopt the philosophy after all. Mightn't be fair to the people who know me. The other fish in my kettle."

He turned toward Waggoner. "Did you know, Charles, that Mr. Mears is known as 'The Pathfinder of the West?'"

Waggoner shook his head.

Wells went on. "The railway line you traveled on the last stretch of your journey here, and the line that connects Telluride to Rico and Durango to the south, and every road in this part of the state were all engineered and constructed by him."

Mears held up his hands. "Zat's not all true, Mr. Vells. I 'ad someone helpink me on vone of ze roads vone day vhen I did not feel so vell." Mears led the laughter at his own joke. "Yes, zose vere ze days," he said. "Ze good old days. Out in ze comfort of bad veather for veeks and months. Many times ze food a starvink man vould not eat. Dynamite zat got vet and vouldn't explode or vent off early and made ze rock come down around you like ze cannon balls. And ze Utes maybe hidink everyvhere and vatchink every tree you chopped and tunnel you cut and beink less and less happy vith you." He shook his head. "Many, many men died to build ze roads. Good men. Vhite men and Red men. I never blamed ze Indians for attacking us. It vas zere land zat ve vere takink from zem. But I could not allow zem eider to stop us. I learned Shoshone so zat I could talk to zem and I tried to make peace vith zem vhenever I could. But zere vere always troubles vith some. And zen zere vas sickness and avalanche and rock slides and mud slides, sometimes attacks by bears and lions. Ze good old days, for sure."

Wells held up his glass of wine.

"To you, Mr. Mears," he proposed. "To the wonder of your industry and accomplishment. And to you, Mr. Brown. To all that you have braved and done to settle this land for we Johnny-come-latelies who have none of your fortitude or endurance. And to your wives, your long unions with them being better testimony than any road or any map of your good works and wisdom. Cheers."

꧁ ꧁ ꧁

Waggoner chuckled aloud again as the Studebaker coasted down the mountain. Wells had been the most eloquent person he had ever known. Words came to him the way breath itself came to others. He had no need to think of what to say, and what he said always sounded as if he had thought it through with the most careful possible consideration before he spoke. It was a gift that Waggoner envied him — as he had envied him in so many ways in those years.

꧁ ꧁ ꧁

When dessert was served, fresh fruit awash in liqueur and set alight with a whoosh of combustion that drew approving applause, then spooned generously onto fresh vanilla ice cream, James Brown rose and proposed a toast to the man across from him, a Rothschild. Brown told the guests that a deal had been struck that day to sell the great Tomboy claim and all of its operation to the Rothschild syndicate.

"To the new owners," he said lifting his glass. "May they mine many millions of dollars here and find peace and joy in our town."

The guests cheered with gusto. Waggoner later learned that the Tomboy had sold for over two million dollars, a record price. The new owners did, indeed, extract enough gold over the coming years to make many millions of dollars profit, more than enough by far to make the price paid seem but a pittance. Peace and joy, however, had proved more difficult to come by.

After his uncle's dinner party, Waggoner had allowed himself to be persuaded to go out on the town with Bulkeley Wells. He had tried to decline. He was not anxious to experience the town's nightlife, which he understood could get out of hand easily. Wells would accept no demurral.

"Come on, old man," he urged. "I have some college friends visiting from back East. They're great fun. I know you'll like them. Have you ever played faro or roulette?"

"No," said Waggoner without admitting that his gambling was, to that point, limited to Bingo.

"Well, then," laughed Wells, taking him by the arm and sweeping him down Oak Street toward the noise and lights of town. "Prepare yourself to reap the rewards of beginner's luck."

They went to The Gold Band, where Wells' friends were in high spirits. They were fresh-faced and soft young men, Waggoner thought, with none of Wells' aplomb, and he did not like them so much. It was a mixed crowd in the gambling hall, and Waggoner and Wells in their fancy clothes and the Harvard swells with their clean-shaven, pink faces and their cackles of hilarity stood out among the other men who were there drinking and smoking and wagering. Waggoner was surprised that there were women there as well, some of them quite beautiful, though with a propensity toward powder on their faces colored over by rouge. Their dresses were not inexpensive looking, but they were of a style that he knew would have raised eyebrows at the party he had just left. Wells' friends treated the women as if they owned them and, though the women didn't seem to mind, Waggoner found it unbecoming. The thought did not occur to him that the women were working, that they got a small cut of the money that they were encouraging Wells' friends to part with in profligate amounts for whiskey and champagne.

Wells noted Waggoner's awkwardness in the company of his Harvard friends. He bought a round of drinks for the others and then led Waggoner to another room where the roulette tables were. They joined a table where the players and the dealer seemed to be on familiar terms with Wells. Waggoner's luck was, indeed, good. Wells' was not. He seemed not to mind, but took great delight in Waggoner's good fortune and coaxed him to increase his bets. Waggoner soon had a month's salary or more piled in front of him and with almost every spin of the wheel, it grew. His nervousness subsided and disappeared, and he felt only the heady thrill of winning. It seemed that with his winnings came a change in others as well. Men he didn't know came to the table to watch him play, offering him drinks and cigars. A woman came and stood behind him and rubbed his shoulders, the scent of her, like a field of flowers, mixing with the smell of smoke and subtly penetrating into his nostrils. It was then that the thought dawned that she was not a paying customer, but any prudishness he might have ordinarily felt was gone.

From simple placements on red or black, even or odd, high – low, Waggoner began to augment his bets by choosing columns and corners, trio and split bets and even straight up bets wagering on a single number. The odds went up as his betting became riskier. From 1:1 on his first simple bets, they grew to 11:1, 17:1, and, even, in the case of a straight up, 35:1. He won less frequently that way, but if and when he did, it more than made up for the losses.

Waggoner could have happily stayed all night at the table. He felt in himself an almost delirious power coming from the stacks of chips that multiplied before him. They conferred on him a stature that he had never known. Sitting with a large take rendered unimportant where he was from or whether he had any claim to importance. At the table, then and there, he was the best, and he relished the feeling. Wells' friends had come to the back room from time to time, progressively high on alcohol, and placed large and foolish bets. Then they reeled back to the front of the house from where their strident bursts of drunken celebration could be heard. And then there was a different tone to the shouting, and one of the college friends stumbled back to Wells' and Waggoner's table, the flush of his face drained.

"There's trouble," he slurred to Wells, trying to pull him from his chair. "It's Derrick. A man's got a knife."

Wells pushed his chair back and excused himself from the table. Waggoner joined the rest of the room as it cleared to follow him. In the front, a space had cleared around one of Wells' friends and another man who had lifted him nearly up on to his toes by the point of a large knife stuck menacingly beneath his chin. The man was clearly in a rage and called the easterner by every epithet he knew, challenging him to say so much as one word back and find his tongue sliced through and licking the floor.

Wells strode into the cleared space and bade the man to put his knife away.

"Fuck you," snarled the knifeman. "You're as big a cunt as your friend here. Say another fucking word and I'll cut the both of ya into fancy fucking-ass bacon."

Wells smiled, a look of rage coming into his eyes that matched his friend's assailant, save that it was cold. He flicked his hand with a swift short movement and a derringer appeared in it from inside his sleeve. He stepped up to the knifeman and held it to his head and cocked it.

"This little gun has not much range," he said almost in a whisper. "But I believe you are now in it. Drop your knife or I will introduce a new hole to your head. It will not be as big as your mouth hole, but it will be quite as ugly."

The knifeman seemed to consider his options for a moment. "Drop it," Wells warned him again, and still the other man hesitated. He shouldn't have. So quickly that Waggoner and the others there could scarcely tell what happened, Wells in one motion pushed his friend away and rapped his gun with a sickening thud against the knifeman's temple. He fell unconscious to the floor and his knife clattered free. Wells stooped and picked it up.

"Tell him I have no hard feelings," he said to no one in particular. "I hope that he will have none of his own. If he chooses to cross me for this, he had better have more than threats, for I will kill him."

Neither Waggoner nor anyone in the room doubted what he said.

CHAPTER FOUR

Alta Cassietto woke up early to catch the first train to Delta. The light of dawn was diffuse and the air was crisply cool. The mornings had been just this way for the past week, and the days had been gloriously bright and clear and warm. Today, she thought, would be just the same, but the morning hinted of colder weather that could come at any time. Usually the first real snow to settle in town did not come until Halloween. The peaks were invariably covered sooner, and there could always be a sudden storm that coated the town temporarily, even in mid-summer. The weather in the mountains was capricious. As "Dad" Painter, publisher and editor of the *Journal* for four decades, was fond of saying, only fools and strangers tried to predict it.

It was to the *Journal*'s offices that Alta hurried before crossing town to the depot. No one else was there yet. Even in the days when there had been plentiful news to report, the paper had never been much of an early-morning enterprise. Late nights, yes, and often, but early in the morning the offices were deserted as a rule. Alta loved being alone there. The rooms held for her the very history of Telluride, not just in the headlines of the framed front pages on the office walls that chronicled the town's passage of years, but in the air, the floorboards, the presses, and desks. She couldn't express it, and would have been embarrassed to try, but it seemed to her that she could feel the soul of Telluride in those empty rooms.

She went to her desk and chose a notepad from among several and sharpened a clutch of pencils. She put the supplies in her bag, along with her press credentials. She scribbled notes in the margins of an article she was working on about yet another mine closure, thoughts that had come to her before she had fallen asleep the night before, and that she had been happy to find were still with her when she woke. Then she went out and knew by the quality of the morning air, the tone of the light, the degree of quiet, that she was still in good time to catch the train.

She was excited to be getting out of town for a day on a paid excursion. She looked forward to the ride over Dallas Divide, the views of the St. Sophia and the Cimarron ridgelines across the undulant mesa ranchland that swept down to Ridgway. From Ridgway to Montrose, and then to Delta, where the track was flat and the views less stunning, she had decided she would work on a larger piece that she had first conceived with the editor that spring. She had worked on it now and then throughout the summer. It was partly something to keep busy with as local news, like the economy, waned unremittingly. It was also a labor of love. It concerned Telluride's history from its earliest days through the peak times in the 1890s and the "troubles" that soon followed, when the miners and mine owners waged a brutal and bloody war against each other, leaving a lingering mistrust that had never really disappeared.

The Rio Grande Southern train, still the old-fashioned narrow-gauge type, was waiting at the station. Alta took a seat by a window, nodding and smiling at familiar faces. She hoped no one would sit beside her and ply her with questions. She had had enough of that since the Anise Koen story first broke. She had been surprised and disappointed by how unkindly, even maliciously, people had judged Anise. People who scarcely knew her were scurrilous in their attacks, and people who had known and liked her were equally shameless in her abandonment. Alta had known Anise socially, but not well. She had regarded her as a bright and attractive young woman with potential for great success. The two women were of the same age and both were independent and ambitious. It was natural that they would have had a mutual admiration, Alta thought, even though they were never close. She felt a little guilty that she had not done more, gone more out of her way, to welcome and befriend the other woman when Anise and her mother had first arrived in town. But Anise had seemed to need no special hospitality; she had fit in quickly and easily.

On the platform the conductor blew his whistle, waved to the engineer, and jumped aboard as the train jerked into motion. Alta thought of Anise as she had seen her in March, shortly after her arrest for embezzlement. She was being held at the county jail pending a jail bond being posted. The jail was a short distance from the offices of the *Journal*. It was strategically located in the heart of the town's once-thriving red light district where arrests had been particularly common in the old days. Directly to the south was Popcorn Alley, so called because the sound of the doors closing behind the prostitutes who plied their trade there was as regular and brisk as corn being popped. The jail was a thick-walled, squat, stone building that had hosted no shortage of drunks, cheats, thieves, and even murderers over the years. Before she went to see Anise there, Alta had never stepped foot inside.

The woman inside the small, bare cell was not unrecognizable, but she wore an expression of woe that altered her features considerably. Her high cheek bones, normally a point of allure, now served to make her face drawn and her eyes darkened and sunken. Once identifiable as a free spirit, she now had the marked air of a trapped animal. Alta had been quite shocked by the transformation. Anise seemed comforted to see her and eagerly accepted a cigarette, which she smoked quickly and nervously.

Alta had come as a reporter, but she asked no probing questions and took no notes. The story, whatever its details, was evident to see on Anise's drawn face, in the way she tightly hugged herself, in the distracted way she moved and spoke, broke eye contact. Alta felt a deep sympathy and sorrow for her. And so she refrained from any form of interview and simply offered quiet company. At one point, in the middle of telling Alta something inconsequential, talking for the sake of it, Anise's face furrowed, her eyes pinched shut, and she covered them with trembling hands and broke down in sobs that she tried to control but could not. Alta held her. She spoke to her in a soft steady stream of words that she somehow found to say without thinking. Slowly, Anise regained herself. She wiped her eyes and apologized. She tried to smile as well, but the look of despair in her eyes did not diminish, and it was that look that Alta took with her when her visiting time was over.

At the end of the Telluride valley, a flat stretch of grass and wetlands where cattle grazed, the San Miguel River began a steep rocky tumble to descend a thousand feet in less than half a mile before it was joined by its southern fork and leveled out again. Where the river began its sharp descent, the train swung away, its track arcing around and down more gradually, cut into the steep side of the cross-sectioned canyon that had been eroded over millennia by glaciers and the river. At the bottom, the train crossed the southern fork and turned back to the main river and ran beside it due west. Alta watched from her window for wildlife. It was not unusual to see bears and even mountain lions; eagles, elk, and bighorn sheep were even likelier. It was beautiful country, dramatic and inspiring, vast and untamable. Thinking of Anise, Alta appreciated the mountains' limitless openness more than ever.

The early sunlight glinted gem-like against the waters of the San Miguel. The water was like skin, Alta thought — perfectly supple, covering its course with an exact but effortless precision. Where the water met a rock or boulder, it wrinkled and adapted itself just as skin adapts to the bend of a finger or a wrist or an elbow. The gentle flow that she regarded with admiration, Alta knew well, was perfectly capable of transforming into a flood of destruction. She had been just a girl when the Trout Lake dam above Ames, upriver on the San Miguel's southern fork, broke. The dam's collapse had been gradual, at first, but irremediable. Word came to town of a breach and whole parties of sightseers, both eager and anxious and including Alta and her mother, rushed by horseback and carriage out of town, past Society Turn, to view the rising flow of the river. At a point, the combined pressure of the lake waters and the weakening resistance of the dam colluded to blow the breach wide open. Alta and the others gathered along the side of the road, looking down on the southern fork as it came directly toward them hundreds of feet below, gave a collective gasp of fear and fascination. A wall of water eight feet high had come into view, a deep froth of foam preceding it; trees and boulders were caught in its irresistible clutch, dirt and mud scalped deeply from the river bed and its banks contributing to its hue of stale, spent blood that contrasted sharply with the yellowed foam and the clear waters ahead of it.

"Dear Lord!" expostulated one of the women near Alta, but otherwise everyone was in a shocked silence. When the floodwater was halfway to them, a great noise became audible to the viewers. It was a din that Alta could still recall with clarity and it gathered in intensity as the flood sped closer. In her diary she had described it as "the sound of doom, an inferno fueled rather than extinguished by water, a roar of violence that swelled with every moment of its accelerating advance until it filled the entire canyon and even the sky above us."

Sometimes, mused Alta as she watched the gleam and sparkle of light on the San Miguel from the train window, life can be like a roaring wall of water that suddenly breaks loose in a mad descent and sweeps up everything in its path. She imagined that Anise must feel just such tumult and helplessness in her life. It wasn't as if she could defend Anise's embezzlement. But she could empathize. Business had always been played fast and loose in Telluride, and the history of the town often seemed to her to be, in large part, a chronicle of people succumbing to the temptation of easy money. The law, and its enforcement, had never been in very close concert with the rest of life there.

From its earliest days of wildcat speculation, Telluride had always been something of an outlaw town. The tangle of claims that had arisen within just five years of the first major strikes in 1875 was complex, overlapping, and had radiated in all directions. Disputes over claim boundaries and incidents of fraud were rife. Matters were as often settled out of court as in. Claim jumpers, as well as rightful owners, were as likely to come away from confrontations with a hole full of hot lead as they were a judge's verdict. In later years, it was commonplace for miners to steal gold-bearing dust by combing it into their greased hair and to spirit high-grade ore pellets out of the mines in many-pocketed vests worn under their shirts, or by dropping them into cans at the outhouse that were attached to fishing line. Arguments over high-stakes gambling or the favors of a soiled dove or a dance hall girl ended regularly in gunplay or at the point of a sharp blade.

What Anise had done was wrong. Alta was in no quandary about that. She had been entrusted with the management of public funds and she had abrogated that responsibility. She deserved consequences. But prison, possibly a sentence of several years, seemed harsh to Alta. Surely, she reasoned to herself, there were other ways to mete out justice. She understood that the law was, needed to be, impersonal: that it could not make distinctions between every instance of crime or tailor itself to every perpetrator. Still, acts of crime, just as acts of love or compassion or devotion, were personal. There was personal motivation, personal history, personal circumstance underlying and infusing the decision to commit crime. Alta did not know what those personal details were in Anise's case, but she thought they should be explored and understood by the arbiters of justice before they summarily condemned her to a prison cell. What benefit to society was it, Alta wondered, to take a bright, industrious person like Anise who was guilty of a lapse of judgment and honesty involving less than four thousand dollars, her first offense and first blemish in an otherwise shining record, and put her in jail? Surely there were other, better ways to deal with such a case.

At a bend in the river a fisherman stood in the shallows and cast his line upstream with a slow deliberate motion, his target a pool below two rocks that interrupted the flow of the river's water and caused it to circle back on itself in an eddy. Alta's father had been fond of fishing and had taught her the simple magic of tying flies and choosing the right ones for different times of day and different conditions. She had often gone with him when he fished, sitting on the river bank admiring the graceful fluidity of his casts, jumping up excitedly when he hooked a trout and helping him net it. She was not in the least squeamish about holding the fish and backing the barbed hook out of its mouth. She did it quickly and efficiently as her father had shown her. If the hook was deeply embedded, or if the fish was big and willful, she did not give up or relinquish the job to her father. Many of the girls in Telluride, when she was growing up, would not consider holding a cold, slippery fish in their hands, let alone try to extricate a hook from it. They paled at Alta's tales of fishing and hunting adventures with her father, of gutting and skinning deer and beaver, of snapping the necks of wounded grouse. None of any of those things had ever bothered Alta. What had always bothered her was hypocrisy. The same girls that blanched at the mention of killing, skinning, or cleaning the internalia out of an animal showed no such qualms about eating the animal or about wearing its hide or fur.

Alta smiled to herself. She supposed she must have seemed a very odd creature to her friends and schoolmates, the first one, always, to cry if someone else was treated unfairly, the last to cry over a skinned knee or a bee sting or the death of a pet whose time had come.

As she had promised herself, Alta took out her notebook after Ridgway to work on her piece about historical Telluride. Her research was largely confined to two main sources: old newspapers and old-timers. She regretted that she had not taken better advantage of the latter when she had been younger and there had been more of them around. Still, she felt lucky to be able to talk to people like Wayne Nostaja, who had been a Western Union messenger, and Missouri Bill, who had been caretaker for the Lone Tree Cemetery for better than thirty years. And, of course, Dad Painter had been a wealth of information and stories. It was from him that she learned about the first explorers to walk along the San Miguel in the Telluride valley, about the Spaniards who had traveled north from Mexico and Santa Fe. They were in the San Juans mining surface gold and silver ore in the eighteenth century, before 1765. They kept no records, as they did not want to give the Spanish king his "Royal Fifth," a twenty percent share of everything of value discovered in the New World and decreed by the king as his personal right. Discoveries of ancient Spanish coins and shored-up shafts provided evidence, however, of the explorers' activities. Hostile Indians, isolation, and long supply lines made their business dangerous. They often buried the treasure they discovered to be recovered later. Mines became lost, but legends survived. The greatest of them was that the Mother Lode — the fabled source of all ore — was to be found in the San Juans.

Alta gazed out her window at the recalcitrant serration of the Cimarron peaks. It amazed her to think that men had braved such fearsome terrain so long ago in desperate search of something that had no more intrinsic value than any other rock except, perhaps, by virtue of its scarcity. It seemed to her a paradox that the first people to arrive in these mountains, the Utes, had put greater value on an eagle feather or a deerskin than they would ever have put on a rock, whatever its mineral content.

If not for the Spanish, and their introduction to the Indians of the horse, the Utes would not have come to be an integral part of the history of Telluride. The San Miguel valley was too remote, its winters too long and harsh, to accommodate visitors reliant on foot travel. By the time the snows had abated enough in spring to allow penetration of the mountains to the valley's rich grass and woodlands and fishing, it would have been almost immediately time to begin the journey back to avoid the early snows of winter.

It had been from an English geologist, Cecil Rupertson, who had worked for many years for the great Smuggler-Union Mine until it shut down just the previous year, that Alta had learned of the prehistory of Telluride. It had been difficult for her to grasp the enormity of time involved in the formation of the mountains that she loved. It made her life seem as fleeting and ephemeral as a moth's. The San Juan Mountains, Rupertson had explained, are an uplifted dome of mostly ancient sedimentary formation overlain by volcanic rock. Volcanic activity, he estimated, had lasted for a period of some fifty million years. Beginning about twenty-five million years ago, it had turned particularly violent. During this later explosive period, warping and folding of the older sedimentary beds occurred, creating faults and fissures. Some of these became injected with the white-hot mineral juices that oozed from the Earth's core as magma.

Alta recalled Rupertson, usually as expressive as a hitching post, becoming genuinely animated as he talked to her of the magma, or "mineralized solutions," as he had put it, cooling and becoming, with the rocks they were mixed with, an ore-rich network of crisscrossing gold and silver veins. Glaciers and erosion later served to carve the landscape into its dramatic contours of cirques and horns and tarns. The last glacier that covered Telluride was ten thousand years ago, a blink in geological terms, said Rupertson. A wedge of ice and snow two thousand feet thick had covered the valley. That glacier, moving at an imperceptible pace but with colossal erosive force, left behind Telluride's rugged steep-walled canyon.

Alta reviewed her notes. They were written in a small, hurried, spidery script that would have been illegible to anyone else and that she herself sometimes had difficulty making out. Given the magnitude of time that it had taken to form Telluride's landscape, it was all the more striking, she thought, how quickly the town had developed. In 1875 there had been nothing and no one in the valley to greet the first prospectors, apart from occasional small parties of Utes. Twenty years later, the town was at the peak of its boom, supporting a population of over five thousand made up of an extraordinarily rich cast of characters drawn from every part of the world. From millionaire mine owners to penniless hermits, the breadth of Telluride's population was as wide as any town's, anywhere in the world. In addition to the miners, who came from Scandinavia, Germany, Italy, Russia, Greece, and especially the British Isles, there were gamblers and cardsharps, gunslingers, mule skinners, and bull-whackers.

Alta squinted to read a note about bull-whackers. It said that a good one could flick a fly in half from twenty feet away.

There were prostitutes, of course, and lots of them. From her research, Alta had learned that in 1895, there were close to two hundred active whores and madams working the south side of town. Each madam was taxed one hundred and fifty dollars a week by the town council, monies that helped considerably to keep the town operating profitably. Girls were recruited to Telluride from all over the country by madams and their agents. They were seduced, lured, lied to, drugged, and dragged. Some fell into the trade because of hard times, abandonment, breakup of a marriage or a romance, or some other crisis, usually financial. For some, the libertine lifestyle was appealing and the ability to sell their bodies was a source of pride and power. Most cases by far, though, were sad and often tragic.

There were, as well, dance hall girls, saloon girls, and theater girls, some of whom, depending on the price offered and their desires, would bed a man for money.

There were investors from as far away as Shanghai. There were famous actors and musicians who were brought to Telluride by private train, straight from performances in San Francisco and New York, in order to perform before the Telluride community. It was a town that lived around the clock, bursting at the seams with optimism, faith, and determination. "The Paris of the West," it had been labeled; also, "a town without a bellyache."

As quickly as it had waxed, Alta had jotted in her nearly indecipherable hand, the town had waned. Closure of the Smuggler-Union had been just the latest and largest of a series of mine closures that had, progressively, jolted Telluride's well-being. From over five thousand, the town's population was now under one thousand, and dropping.

Alta shrugged and shook her head. It was no good letting her thoughts carry on in a negative vein. If she did, she knew she would soon contemplate the town's complete demise. Alta was not a fatalist, but lately it had been hard for her to keep her outlook positive. That was, perhaps, why the historical piece was so engrossing: It was an escape. She especially enjoyed researching the earliest years, when the young town was infused with prospectors' unbridled optimism.

She scanned another page of notes and her eye stopped at a name that had been underlined: Bulkeley Wells. Of all the historical characters in Telluride, she thought, none so embodied the town's verve and vitality as Wells. And none evoked a more passionate response, good and bad, from those who knew him. To some he was heroic. To others he was the devil incarnate. Alta remembered him distinctly: He was a striking character, one that any woman would notice immediately, tall and almost impossibly handsome. She had lost count of the women who had told her, matter-of-factly, that Wells was far and away the most handsome man they had ever met and the most charming. Even the most staid old spinsters would soften at mention of his name and, in speaking of him, grow lyrical. He was, in a word, glamorous.

He was also extremely wealthy, although not necessarily by his own right. Alta had not been able to determine precisely, but she believed that Wells' family, from Chicago, was socially prominent, but of no great financial stature. Money, however, was attracted to Wells like filings to a magnet. He had been closely allied to Harry Payne Whitney, one of America's most successful and prominent investors. The story that Alta had heard from several sources was that Wells, shortly after graduating from Harvard, was at a men's club in New York City and was invited to join a game of cards. The stakes were ten dollars a point, not an inconsequential wager. Wells misunderstood, thinking the stakes were just a dollar a point. At such a price, he felt comfortable coolly bluffing his way through a number of bad hands. Playing at the table was Whitney. He was most impressed by Wells' sangfroid, as well as by his educational background in mining and engineering. Virtually on the spot he engaged Wells to act as his agent, charging him with identifying profitable opportunities in western mining ventures.

As if that were not enough, Wells shortly thereafter became engaged and, in 1895, married one of Boston's leading debutantes, Grace Livermore. Wells' new father-in-law, Colonel Thomas Livermore, made a sizeable fortune working and then selling a copper mine in Calumet, Michigan. Livermore invested a share of his profits in a fledgling gold mining operation in Telluride later to become known as the Smuggler-Union. It was destined to be one of the three biggest and most profitable mines in Telluride, and Bulkeley Wells would be its manager.

In addition to investing millions of dollars for Whitney and marrying into wealth, Wells also came to attract the admiring eye of Denver's premiere socialite, Mrs. Crawford Hill. Crawford Hill's wealth was well in excess of Colonel Livermore's and not far shy from Whitney's. Like both of them, he had substantial equity in mining ventures. At his wife's persuasion, he enlisted the service of Bulkeley Wells to augment his holdings.

Wells was perfectly disposed to operate as nexus for these three channels of wealth, Alta had concluded. In addition to consummate charm and good looks, he was cultured and exuded a sense of inviolable self-confidence. From the moment he stepped off his private train car in the spring of 1896, Wells had Telluride in his expensively tailored pocket.

Alta closed her eyes and mused. The rich and glamorous profile that Wells presented was only one side of his character, just as it was only one side of Telluride's. Both had a darker side. For the miners that Alta knew personally, including her father who had lived through the troubles at the turn of the century, there continued a bitter sense of hostility that hardened their eyes and clipped their words when they spoke of Wells. It had been at the Smuggler-Union in 1899 that the Fathom System, so odious to miners, so heralded by mine owners, had been introduced to Telluride. The system was comparable to piece work, with a miner being paid for a set amount of work rather than for an amount of time. The fathom was the measure of performance — a six-foot long, six-foot high section of rock that was as wide as the vein being worked. The miners, under this system, could, and often did, earn less than the standard three dollars a day. With one dollar taken out for room and board and net of expenses for tools, gloves, dungarees, and any other personal essentials that they might be missing and need to buy from the mine store, many miners found themselves work-ing twelve-hour days but unable to get out of the company's debt. Meanwhile, the owners, many of whom, such as Livermore and Whitney, were absentees, were realizing enormous profits. And the twelve-hour days, regularly seven days a week, were filled with hazards and conditions potentially, and many times actually, lethal.

The Western Federation of Miners, to which Alta's father had been an early member, seized on the Fathom System to unite the Telluride mine workers. The Federation's constitution had been one of the few books written in English that Alta remembered ever seeing in her father's lap. More often than not its pages were unturned as he slept and snored in his easy chair. Alta had often read the book for him. She could still recall the preamble of the constitution verbatim:

> *Men engaged in the hazardous and unhealthy occupation*
> *of mining should receive fair compensation for their labor*
> *and such protection from the law as will remove needless*
> *risk to life and health.*

Even as a young girl, Alta had considered those words especially eloquent and compelling in their honest simplicity. In a reverie now, she imagined Bulkeley Wells tearing the page from the book and shred-ding it into pieces or holding it to a flame. No one in Telluride had been more fiercely anti-union than Wells, and by his violent vigilante crusade against unionists, he became the symbol of all that was evil to the miners.

The train was slowing as it approached Montrose. Alta closed her notebook. History was complicated, she acknowledged to herself. Understanding it and recounting it was as challenging as maintaining objectivity in journalism. Facts, she was becoming more and more convinced, were variable. Steadfast truth was hard to come by, perhaps even impossible. So much, she felt, was colored and shaded by per-spective and interpretation. Bulkeley Wells was a prime example. Had he been a hero or a monster? Had he been selfless, as was argued by his supporters, or self-serving, as decried by his detractors? Even the famous story of his surviving an assassination attempt when a bomb had exploded underneath his bed — a story that had helped to garner him a reputation for courage and to enlist antipathy towards the union miners — was suspect. She had heard it said by more than one old-time miner that the bombing was a hoax, a piece of theater, devised by Wells himself. Ultimately, the truth was impossible to ascertain, and Wells was unavailable for comment. He had left Telluride a few years ago under a cloud of scandal, divorced for desertion, cut off from his wealthy sponsors, bound for speculative oil and gas ventures in California that, it was widely rumored, had not panned out.

The train lumbered into the Montrose station, its brakes emitting intermittent squeals. Many of the passengers who Alta had boarded with rose to gather their things. It occurred to Alta that most, perhaps all, of the departing passengers knew Anise Koen. They had, undoubtedly, seen her regularly in Telluride, spoken to her, possibly dealt with her at County Hall regarding their taxes. She wondered how many of them knew or cared that sentence on her would be passed today. Not many, she imagined. People were careful with their feelings, she knew. And, when their opinions or preconceptions were countered, they often reacted with anger. People were more comfortable, Alta considered, with black and white than with gray. Black and white was easier, neater. So, regardless of what they may have thought of Anise before, however competent, friendly, or helpful they may have found her, they were now more at ease dismissing her, condemning her, placing her in a section of their thoughts that was as cold and spare and inescapable as the jail cell where Alta had last seen her. Alta almost wished that she could do the same.

CHAPTER FIVE

Anise Koen lay in her cot on her uncomfortable mattress and willed her mind to calm. Although the first brittle light of dawn had begun to filter through her cell window, she had been awake for hours. This was the day that she had both looked forward to and dreaded for many weeks. Foolishly, childishly, she had somehow been able to persist in the fantasy that her predicament, if not sooner than at least today, would end. Her age, her prior record, her promising character or just a stroke of luck, some divine reversal of fortune, she had held out hope, would allow her life — her normal life — to be returned to her. Today was the last day for that to happen. Today she would be sentenced by Judge Bruce. Her plea would be guilty. She had been able to see no other choice.

At seven o'clock, Matron came to wake her. She found Anise already washed and dressed. She had powdered her face so that the dark circles of sleeplessness and worry under her eyes were less apparent. She had applied, as well, a touch of lipstick and rouge. She wore a fetching new outfit that her mother had brought her, and, sitting on the edge of her cot, she was the picture of a sophisticated young lady with the world at her beckoning. Only her eyes told a different story.

Anise ate only a little breakfast, not even finishing her coffee. At eight o'clock, her mother came to see her but could not avoid breaking down in dolorous sobs every few minutes, a tendency that Anise found, in equal parts, upsetting and annoying. She prevailed on Matron to escort her mother away.

At nine o'clock, Walter Hillman came. He was as awkward, tight-lipped, and tired looking as he had been before, but Anise was not unhappy to see him. The look of pain that he wore evoked in her a solicitude that helped her ignore her own worry and fear. She again found herself coaxing him to talk. He struggled through a series of responses to her questions, but there was something so obviously distressing him that she stopped and asked him directly what was the matter. He hesitated just a moment, a conflict of emotions displayed in his tired eyes. Then, in a hoarse whisper, he poured forth a confession.

"I've taken money from the bank. Only small amounts, nothing big. I don't even know why I did it, really. It wasn't as if I was desperately hard up. It was just the timing. I honestly meant to return it. All of it. The thing is, though, there's more missing. A lot more. I think it may be as much as fifty thousand, perhaps more. I think the president is responsible. There's no one else it could be, but I don't know what to do. I think he's found out that I've taken funds and will try to turn the whole thing against me. He wouldn't go down on his own, I know that — he's not the type. He'll do whatever he has to to save his skin." Hillman stopped, his face tight with misery.

Anise was silent. It was the last thing in the world that she had expected to hear. At the same time, it could hardly shock her. And it certainly made sense of Hillman's visits and reticence. She realized that she was probably the only person in the world to whom her visitor felt comfortable confiding.

"My family will be devastated if they find out," Hillman went on, his voice strained, "utterly and completely devastated. I come from a very respectable family, and the scandal will destroy them. I know it will. And I know it will come out soon. The state commissioner, McFerson, is cracking down just now because so many banks are going under. We're scheduled for an examination. There simply isn't any way that fifty thousand can be covered up. Even if I'm not accused of stealing it all, I'll be found out for what I did take, when our books and records are fully inspected. This fellow McFerson is supposed to be tough. They say he's trying to make a name for himself, that he has plans to go into politics. He's promised to clean up every bank in Colorado. He's already shut down many. Looks as if we may be next."

Anise had heard of Grant McFerson. Whether or not he had political aspirations, she did not know, but he certainly had public recognition. Over the past months there had not been many days when his name was not in the papers. There had been a rash of bank failures throughout the state. Some had resulted from hard times in mining and agriculture, some from fraud and defalcation. McFerson had made it his vigorously repeated intention to clean and tighten the system. She even remembered a quote of his reported by the *Journal* in Telluride. He said he wanted a state banking system in which "honest bankers could be protected from crooked customers and honest customers protected from crooked bankers."

"So," said Anise, "have you come to see me for a foretaste of what it will be like for you?" It was a mean thing to say, and she saw that

Hillman was stung sharply. "I'll tell you this," she went on quickly, sorry that she had spoken without thinking and had hurt her visitor. "Take a good look at your friends. If you are unfortunate enough to wind up in this place, or anywhere like it, their number will reduce drastically. If you have even one left, you will consider yourself lucky."

"I'm not so worried about friends. It's my family that I worry about — my father and my brother and sister." Hillman's voice trailed off and he bowed his head in remorse.

Anise eschewed any attempt to placate him. She didn't feel he had come to her for that. He had come to her for confession but not absolution. She put back to him the question that he had posed to her on his first visit.

"Why did you do it?"

Hillman looked at her without replying immediately.

"I've asked that of myself a thousand times," he replied eventually. "I truly don't know if I have an answer. Or maybe not one I could put into words. It wasn't greed. And it wasn't need, really, either. One never seems to have enough money, of course, but that wasn't it. Not really."

He paused, intent on trying to at last express, to the one person he knew might understand, what force, what motivation, had pushed him to take what he was charged with safekeeping.

"I think..." he started and paused again. "I think I did it because I felt invisible. Do you know what I mean?"

Anise nodded.

"I felt as if my life was invisible and empty and meaningless. What I do for a living, it seems to me, any trained circus animal could do. I have no real power, can't do what I think should be done. The people who really need help from the bank are considered too risky to deal with. The ones who don't need help, we fight to do business with, offering them premium rates on their deposits and discounted ones on their loans. At the end of the day, the bank cares nothing at all about anything but money. It isn't the people we care about — their lives, their circumstances, their stories. It's just their money. It's all about that, always. And I'm just an agent of the bank, nothing more. I do what I'm expected to, what I'm told to, and make sure I do the best I can with a smile and without letting anyone know how miserably unhappy I am that none of it has anything to do with who I really am."

Hillman's words gushed out in a torrent. It was hard for Anise to credit that he was capable of so many words at once, expressed with such feeling, after her prior pains to get him to say anything at all.

What struck her, too, was that Hillman did not offer his words as any kind of excuse or justification. He was not using them to gain sympathy or understanding. What he was doing was baring his soul. She was certain that he had never done it before.

Anise reached for Hillman's hand and held it. He started to speak again but she stopped him by putting a finger to his lips. After a moment, his eyes filled with tears and he wept silently. Anise was surprised that her own eyes remained dry, and the thought came to her that she might never cry again.

✖ ✖ ✖

The sentencing lasted less than an hour. Apart from Alta and Anise's mother, no one from Telluride was in the courtroom. Witnesses for the prosecution had previously provided their testimonies to Judge Bruce. As Anise's plea was guilty, there were no witnesses for the defense, nor any jury. Anise's attorney pleaded briefly for leniency, citing his client's previously clean record and the difficult times that, he claimed, "were leading to people of even irreproachable character being swayed in their judgment and compromised in their actions." It was an unimpassioned effort, Alta thought, and the judge evidently concurred with her assessment. It took him just a moment after Anise's lawyer had finished to make some notes on his prepared papers before delivering sentence.

"Miss, Koen. You were charged in your capacity as Assistant Treasurer for the County of San Miguel with fiduciary responsibility of public funds. On taking your office, you swore to uphold that responsibility. By your actions, you have broken that solemn pledge. By them, you have demonstrated not only contempt for the public welfare and for the sanctity of your oath but clear criminal intent, as well. This court recognizes your crime not as one of impulse or desperation but as premeditated, a calculated and deliberate effort to willfully advantage yourself of your position of trust to defraud the citizenry and government of San Miguel County for your own personal aggrandizement. The court has noted your attorney's request for leniency, and the reasons offered in support of that request. Although I do not hold that our times are so difficult as to turn honest people into dishonest ones, I do recognize that you are young and of a formerly clean record. I will not therefore sentence you to the maximum possible penalty available to me by statute of the law. Neither, however, will I reduce your sentence to the minimum."

The judge then summoned his bailiffs to bring Anise from her seat to stand in front of him. Alta was impressed that the young woman approached him without falter, her posture erect, her head held high.

"Miss Anise Koen, by order of this court, you will from this day — and for no less than three years hence — be remanded in custody to the state correctional institution situated in Cañon City of this state or to whatever other correctional institution shall be determined by this or any other duly appointed court to hold you. You will not be eligible for parole. Upon your release, you will be prohibited from holding any public office whatsoever in Colorado, and any attempt by you to do so will be punishable by additional incarceration." The judge looked up from his papers and directly at Anise, whose own eyes held his firmly. "I would urge you, Miss Koen, to take advantage of your time in the penitentiary to carefully chart your future freedom. Three years is not an eternity. Upon your release you will still have, God willing, the majority of your life ahead of you. Your conviction will prove a bane to you, of course. But it needn't mean your ruination."

Alta saw that Anise's knees gave just a little, but she recovered herself. The judge bade the bailiffs to escort her from the room. Before she exited, she turned her head toward Alta and smiled a wan, sad smile. Alta recognized it as being nearly identical to the one she thought she had seen on C.D. Waggoner's face just two nights before. Anise disappeared and Alta turned to go. Behind her was a young man, standing and staring at the door through which Anise had walked with the bailiffs. The man looked as if he expected her to reappear. It occurred to Alta that Anise's smile had not been directed at her.

CHAPTER SIX

After Fairplay, Waggoner had slept in the car. It was a fitful sleep, but he found when he awoke that Mary had very capably completed most of the rest of the drive to Denver. It was early afternoon. They were a few hours ahead of schedule. He drove the rest of the way and they arrived at their hotel in time for tea. Waggoner had deliberately chosen a hotel that was not centrally located. Even so, he found himself edgy, expecting any moment to see someone he knew in the lobby. His main fear was that he would see Clarence Downtain, and, as he had driven along the Denver streets, his eyes had darted nervously from side to side and at the oncoming traffic, a dread of recognition roiling his stomach. He knew the chances were extreme, but that knowledge provided scant comfort.

Once in their room, he asked his wife if she would find a pharmacy and buy him some milk of magnesia. She was happy for the chance to stretch her legs. When she had gone, Waggoner went back to the lobby and asked for a private phone for a long-distance call to Seattle. The receptionist directed him to a small room off the lobby and then placed the call. The knot in Waggoner's stomach tightened as he waited for the connection.

The phone rang at the other end three times before a woman's voice answered.

"Hello, Dora? It's Buck Waggoner."

"Mr. Waggoner? Heavens! What a surprise. How are you?"

"Just fine, thank you. How are you?"

"I'm well. I miss Telluride, but Seattle is a fine town, too."

The connection was not strong and Waggoner had to strain to hear. There was an echo as well that caught up with and overtook his words if he spoke too quickly.

"I need a favor, Dora," he said, slowly. He squeezed his eyes shut, not confident even yet that he could actually propose to his former assistant what he wished her to do.

"Of course, Mr. Waggoner. Anything at all."

He opened his eyes and stared unseeing at the wall in front of him. "I need you to send some wires."

"Wires?"

"Yes. Telegrams to New York."

"I see," replied the woman. Notwithstanding the poor connection and the faintness of her voice, Waggoner could clearly hear a note of doubt at the other end of the line. "Who are the wires to?" she asked.

"Banks," he said simply.

"And what are they to say?"

"They are instructions for transfers of funds to the Bank of Telluride's account." There was a long pause that he knew was not accounted for by distance.

"Is there no one there in Telluride to send the instructions?"

"I'm not in Telluride, Dora. I'm away from town on business."

"And Mr. Downtain? Can he not arrange the transfers? Or what of the girl you hired when I left?"

Waggoner squeezed his eyes shut again and held his breath as pain stabbed at his guts. "The thing is, Dora, this is a matter of some urgency. Mr. Downtain is unavailable and the new girl has made mistakes on prior occasions that have resulted in mix-ups and delays that I cannot afford in this instance. I really need your help. I know it seems irregular, but I assure you that it is simply a matter of expediency. I can pay you for your trouble. I thought a thousand dollars would be appropriate."

Again there was a drawn out silence from the other end. The next words he heard were muffled, as if they were being spoken to someone else and deliberately muted by covering the telephone's mouthpiece.

"Mr. Waggoner? I'm afraid I really can't help you. I'm sorry. I would like to, honestly. But what you are asking is..."

Her words cut out, but it didn't matter. The conversation was one that Waggoner had held already in his mind countless times, her response already frequently imagined.

"So, if you wouldn't mind, I'm afraid I'll have to ask that you find someone else."

Waggoner nodded but said nothing.

"Mr. Waggoner? Are you there? I'm very sorry, but I'm sure you understand."

"Yes, Dora. I understand. Thank you, anyway. My regards to your husband."

"Yes, I'll tell him. Our regards to Mrs. Waggoner. And to all our friends in Telluride."

"Yes, indeed. Goodbye, Dora."

"Goodbye, Mr. Waggoner. It was nice to hear from you."

Waggoner replaced the phone and sat slumped. He had but one more option. He had a niece in Denver, Amelia Jones, a girl that he knew would do whatever he asked of her. She had spent most of her summers as a child visiting Telluride and was more of a sister to his son than a cousin. He had not wanted to resort to her, to involve her. He had not wanted to involve any family or friends. He knew, too, that she was still in close touch with Delos, and that the probability was high that she would meet with his son, or speak to him at least, while Delos was in Denver visiting his fiancée. He worried that she would mention him and his request of her. But he had no choice. The wires needed to be sent the next day. As he and his wife made their way to Kansas, instructions to the banks needed to be making their way to New York. If they were received on Thursday, processed on Friday, then funds would be credited and available by Saturday. Sunday, the banks would be closed and Monday, as well, for Labor Day. Tuesday would be too late.

Waggoner dialed his niece's number. He prayed that she would be home. When she picked up, he felt his stomach begin to relax.

※ ※ ※

Waggoner awoke disoriented in his sister's house in Olathe, Kansas. He lay for a minute, composing his mind. He and his wife had arrived in the evening after another long, hard drive. He had retired as early as he could without being rude. He had fallen quickly to sleep. Now, after not nearly enough rest, he was awake and his mind was churning at a rate that he knew would permit no further sleep. In a few hours, he would say good-bye to his wife and be on his way to New York.

It had not been many months since his last visit East. In the spring, he had made the rounds of the Wall Street banks, having called earlier on their Denver correspondent banks. He had endeavored to secure additional loans and lines of credit for both his bank and himself. It had been a grueling and humiliating experience, and one that had met with limited success, too limited by far. He had been particularly galled by the Denver banks' reluctance and, ultimately, refusal to accommodate what he insistently characterized to them as a short-term liquidity issue and not, as they impugned, a solvency one.

How times had turned. Not many years prior, the urban banks had actively solicited business from him. While mining was still vibrant in

Telluride, his bank had been considered a premiere institution and the lowest possible risk. Indeed, before the war, on several occasions, and especially during the Near Panic of 1907, when many banks went under and many more refused to pay out cash, he had been able to supply both the Denver and New York banks with large advances of gold and had maintained substantial deposits with them as well. There had been months when shipments of gold and cash to the very banks that now refused him credit had run well over six figures. He had, at least to a significant degree, helped keep the city banks alive. Now, when circumstances were reversed, those same banks conveniently ignored that history. It was criminal in Waggoner's opinion — inexcusable and untenable.

Without disturbing Mary, Waggoner slipped out of bed. He felt blindly in the dark for his leather satchel and then padded down the hall with it to the kitchen. He quietly closed the door behind him and turned on the light. From the satchel he took a carbon copy of the Western Union wording that he had left with his niece in Denver the day before.

Waggoner studied the copy as if he could read the very future in its words. It was in coded language devised by the American Bankers' Association. He had instructed his niece that the telegrams were to be identically worded, with the exception of one word that specified a dollar amount.

ALLUNGANDO EXEMPLAR CHASE NATIONAL BANK BRINCATUR THE BANK OF TELLURIDE EXAGITE.

Waggoner silently read and re-read the words until they came to be an incantation. Then he put the copy down and, involuntarily, took a deep breath. There was, of course, a possibility that his plan might fail. In fact, there were any numbers of ways that it could unravel. Timing was not the only factor. He would need luck as well. His heartbeat quickened as he contemplated the odds against him and the magnitude of the bluff that he was playing. He thought again of his introduction to gambling so many years ago. He recalled so clearly how intoxicating it had been to win at roulette and, later, his first bluff hand at stud poker. Winning a poker hand legitimately, with strong cards, was exciting. Winning with a bluff was incomparable.

His thoughts turned suddenly to Anise. She had been a gamble of a kind and one that had made him a loss, but he regretted it not at all. If she had asked him to do it again, he would have. It wasn't that he was in love with her, he didn't think. His love was for the woman of whom she so strongly reminded him, a woman with whom he had fallen in love his very first night in Telluride; a woman whom he was fated never to have, however ardently he had wanted her. Anise reminded him so very strongly of Mary Reade.

When he met her in the spring of 1896, she had been just about the same age as Anise and far nearer his twenty-one years than his uncle's forty-six. She was pretty, with a trim figure and dark eyes that flashed brilliantly when she was happy or angry and that clouded over opaquely when she was sad. She was lively and fun, with a mischievous streak that she allowed Waggoner, among few others, to know. She was well-read, well-traveled, a very accomplished horsewoman, and a consummate hostess. Most intoxicating to him had been her smile and her laugh, both of which came to her easily and often.

During the first few weeks of Waggoner's arrival to Telluride, his uncle had been engaged for long stretches, day and night, with the sale of the Tomboy Mine. There were endless meetings with lawyers, surveyors, abstract companies, engineers, and assayers. There were, as well, visits to the mine, tours of its deep shafts and myriad tunnels, inspections of its buildings and equipment, and interviews with its shift bosses and managers. And then, of course, there were dinners at Telluride's best restaurants — long dinners drawn out over several courses and accompanied by fine wines with cigars afterward and brandy, and then, perhaps, before going home, a turn at the gambling tables.

Apart from a few brief interludes, Waggoner scarcely saw his uncle at all in those first weeks. In his absence, his fiancée was charged with showing the new arrival around town, making introductions and keeping him entertained. Waggoner could not have been more pleased with the circumstances. He found his uncle to be quite formal and cold. He had come away from the first brief meetings they had had, their few times together, feeling not unlike he had as a child after a meeting with his school headmaster. With Mary Reade, on the contrary, he was happy and relaxed. Together they went on walks and picnics and took long horseback rides.

Frank and Henrietta Brown had already fully embraced Mary Reade as part of their household and they immediately expanded it to include their nephew as well. The Brown Ranch became a regular destination for excursions from town. Waggoner loved it there; the rough solidity of the fences and corrals, the snug square joints of the house and barn timbers. Best of all were the views. The ranch was located on mesa land south of town and a thousand feet above the valley floor. To the east, the terrain slanted up past cleared pastures and through thick stands of aspen and spruce until it joined the vertical pitch of the Palmyra ridgeline. To the west, the mesa sloped down gradually until it reached a sharp canyon cut by the south fork of the San Miguel River. Across the canyon, the mesa continued, spreading toward a three-peak massif that stood up powerfully against the sky to fourteen thousand feet. The Ute name for the massif, Frank Brown told his nephew, was Shandoka, which meant "Storm Gatherer." Waggoner deemed it a good name, as he came to witness frequent storms wrap around the mountain, rain and snow released with fury on its sharp facets and into the chutes and couloirs that rutted it.

Much farther west, across the Colorado border with Utah, the La Sal Mountains were visible a hundred miles away on clear days. As Shandoka was, the La Sals were capped with snow most of the year.

"That's where they sent the Utes," Frank told his nephew, pointing with his tough chin to the distant range of blue mountains with their white peaks. "On the other side of those mountains is high desert. It's godforsaken country compared to this. Dry, hot, and mean. Beautiful, I guess some might say, but in a devilish way, if you ask me. It's hostile terrain, almost impossible to support life on. Red rock and dead sand is mostly what it is. You can grow rattlesnakes and cactus, but it's not a place much meant for people."

"Who sent them there?"

"The government," Frank had answered. "Washington. It was only a few years after they had signed a treaty with the Utes ceding them rights to four hundred thousand acres here. 'So long as the streams shall flow and the grass shall grow.' That's what they wrote, and they signed it. Well, sir, along John Fallon comes in '75 and he files five claims up in Marshall Basin and hits some pretty decent payrock. Before you know it, there's a rich stink of boom in the air, and the government decides it's maybe not such a grand idea to have given the Utes all this land with streaks of gold and silver running all through it. So they broke the treaty, rounded up the Utes, and shipped them West. Didn't even give them decent transport. And for their troubles, for their sacrifices, Washington agreed to pay them twenty-four thousand dollars a year, but I've seen the form of payment, and it ain't cash. No, sir. The Indians get paid in kind, every year, with a wagon train of goods and produce, most of which is inferior, if not just plain rotten or faulty."

Frank chuckled glumly. "The Utes got the last laugh, though," he said.

"How's that?"

"They put a curse on this valley."

"A curse?" Waggoner presumed his uncle was being facetious.

"Yes sir, a powerful curse. White people scoff, but you ask any Indian about it, and they'll know. Not just the Utes, either. The Comanche, Apache, Navaho — they all know about it. There are things in this world beyond explanation or understanding; things that exist beyond our certain beliefs. When the Utes left here, forced out and betrayed, their medicine men invoked the spirits of their ancestors and of the very roots and rocks of this place for revenge.

"And believe me," Frank stated quietly, fixing his nephew with a clear cool eye, "there is more tragedy here, more death and catastrophe, more loss and heartache than you'll find in any other fifty towns combined. There's a curse here, I don't have any doubt. You see you make sure to stay away from its power and sidestep it whenever you feel it reaching for you."

Waggoner had mentioned his uncle's words to Mary Reade as they rode across an alpine meadow above the ranch.

"I've heard of the Ute curse," she said. "Some people swear that it's true and some that it's impossible. James says that it's just an excuse people use for every hard time or when things go wrong."

"What do you think? Do you think there really can be such a thing?"

Mary Reade was pensive. She reined in her horse and turned in her saddle to face Waggoner.

"Before I came here, I would never have entertained the thought. But there is a power here that I've come to feel. I can't properly describe it, but it has to do with the wild beauty of this place. They say this land was sacred to the Utes. I can believe that. Can I believe in a curse? Perhaps it's not that far of a remove. One thing is certain: There is an incidence of tragedy here that is alarming. Whether that's just the nature of things in the mountains, and with mining, I don't know. I don't take your Uncle Frank's opinions lightly, though.

"Can you keep a secret?" she asked.

Waggoner nodded, a delighted conspirator.

"Frank is teaching me to calf rope. James would die if he knew. And heaven knows what he would say or do to Frank. But I love it. And the calves aren't really hurt by it. In fact, they're quite safe. My lasso misses them far more regularly than not."

Waggoner was happy to keep the secret. If she had told him, in confidence, that the world would explode before the end of the day, he would not have breathed a word to anyone. He would have happily, silently, awaited the world's fiery end, comforted to the last moment by the thought of sharing with her a secret. He was in love. It was beyond any feeling he had ever had. It was a love that was fated never to be requited, and without ever admitting that to himself, he still knew it to be true. He never proclaimed his love. Propriety and his own lack of self-confidence stopped him a hundred, a thousand times. He feared her rejection abjectly. So long as he never actually told her that he loved her, that his very soul was locked in a prison cell to which she alone held the key, he could avoid that rejection. The icy pain of loving her in secret, in silence, was preferable to the incendiary pain of hearing from her lips, or seeing in her eyes, that she did not, would not, have the same feelings for him.

Thirty-three years later, Waggoner still felt a palpable tenderness, a bruise, in his heart when he thought of Mary Reade. The first time he saw Anise Koen, it was as if he had been suddenly pummeled in that very spot. It wasn't that she looked so very much like Mary: It was more to do with the liveliness of her eyes, her slender figure, the ready play of her smile. Then there was the chic tailoring of her clothes and the sweet light scent of her. It was a whole combination of shared characteristics as well as something ineffable, some mysterious combustion of invisible chemicals. Waggoner saw Anise Koen and felt all the delicious, excruciating pain of his love for Mary Reade reignite.

In his sister's kitchen, the first light of day appeared tentatively at the window. Waggoner rubbed his brow and yawned. He felt punchy from travel and lack of sleep. At the same time, a certain electrical excitement tingled in him, the tautness of anticipation. He was committed to the highest stake wager of his life. The odds were not in his favor, but he would play his bluff hand, regardless. He felt as if his life had been propelled inexorably toward a moment of truth and that the moment was imminent.

He rubbed his brow again and pressed his temples with his middle fingers, massaging them. However exciting his gamble was, however it satisfied him to wager everything with an empty hand, he could not shake a vestige of cold dread. Sitting in the dawn's pale illumination, it occurred to him, not for the first time by any means, that the curse of the Utes was something very real indeed, and that, contrary to his uncle's early warning, he had not been able to stay away from it, to sidestep it, keep away from its reach.

CHAPTER SEVEN

Over the years, C.D. Waggoner had been to New York City several times, always on business. Each time he came, though, he was shocked anew by the enormity of the place, by its pace and its noise and the admixture of malodorous scents that were carried by its dirty eddying air. He truly could not fathom how people could live in such a crowded and frenetic environment. It was an unhealthy milieu, he thought, and the people on its streets seemed stricken with varying conditions of unhappiness. No one seemed inclined or prepared to look anyone else in the eye, and smiles were the most precious possible rarity.

The Mansfield Hotel on West 44th Street, just off Fifth Avenue, had been first recommended to him by Bulkeley Wells as a comfortable and quiet choice, and he had never felt the need to stay elsewhere. His visit this time would be a short one, and he had booked a room for just one night. When he checked in, late in the afternoon, there was a telegram waiting for him. It was from Harry Miller — Waggoner's closest friend and the only person, apart from his wife, who knew where to find him. The telegram was terse, even by the minimalist standards of the medium. It read: Anise convicted 3 years state pen.

Waggoner read the brief message only once, but he stared at the words a long time before folding the telegram and tucking it into the inside pocket of his tweed jacket. Then he left his room and went for a walk.

In Telluride he walked nearly every day, a habit that he had adopted early on. Sometimes he walked up the mining road to Bear Creek Falls, sometimes to the end of the canyon where Bridal Veil Falls cascaded in a spectacular free fall, ending in a shroud of mist and a jumble of moss-covered boulders. Most often, though, he walked up the Tomboy Road, sometimes carrying on all the way past Royer's Gulch and through the short tunnel above it that had been blasted through an extrusion of bedrock. The tunnel was known as the Social Tunnel. In the old days, it was where the fallen angels of Pacific Street would come in buggies and carriages to meet the miners on their way down the mountains to town. The miners and the whores would mingle at the tunnel, and partnerships would be formed for the day or the night, or both. For miners who hadn't time enough to go to town, it was popular to escort their choice of the painted ladies back to the Tomboy, where there was an indoor bowling alley and the world's highest soda fountain.

Waggoner would often, as well, turn off the Tomboy early and follow the steep switchback track that ultimately led to the Liberty Bell Mine. Over the years, and through the seasons, he must have taken close to five thousand walks, he guessed. And never once had he become bored of any of Telluride's trails and roads. There seemed to always be something new to see — a change in the coloration of the forest floor, or its canopy, an aspect of a vista that was unique, new snow, new leaves, less snow, fewer leaves, an inimitable dawn, a never-to-be-forgotten sunset; always, there was something that kept his walks from tedium.

Sometimes, particularly on Sundays after church, he took long hikes that lasted all day, following narrow game trails and old Ute paths and scrambling up almost vertical pitches to reach the knife-edge of a high ridge or the summit of a peak. His hikes were not without incident, and he returned home as often as not bloodied and bruised, a knee or ankle twisted, his trousers muddied and torn. For the sake of being completely alone in the mountain wilderness, he would have suffered far more.

The evening air of New York was miasmic compared to what Waggoner was used to. It was textured by grit and the heavy fumes of too many buses and cars. Gusts of wind buffeted the city's glass and concrete canyon walls, seeming intent on escaping their entrapment, only to be doomed to disappointment.

A discarded page of a newspaper blew at Waggoner from twenty paces ahead, as if he was reeling it in with a hook and a line. It attached itself to his leg and he stopped to remove it. It was a page from the *Daily News*. A photograph of someone with a rather grotesque visage, partially obscured by a large slouch hat, caught his eye. The caption beneath identified the person as Mary O'Dey, whom it proclaimed as "the ugliest woman in the world" and who had just arrived in New York from England aboard The Leviathan. Waggoner studied the photograph with the dread fascination that it was intended to provoke. The woman was, he concluded, no beauty, but he doubted that she deserved the dubious honorific she was attributed. He thought of Jew Fanny, madam of The White House in Telluride for many years, who was short and fat, and possessed a pocked and lopsided face that was truly frightening to behold. He suspected that Mary O'Dey was comparatively comely.

On the other side of the page were headlines about the Zephyr, a German dirigible that was completing the first-ever air circumnavigation of the globe. There was a story, too, of a race between women's air teams, one of them headed by Amelia Earhart. Air travel and air speed records had recently become widely covered news stories. It was all very thrilling, Waggoner supposed, but there was nothing, he was certain, that could entice him to defy gravity, particularly not in a machine that could, at any moment, come crashing back to earth. He folded the paper and deposited it in a litterbin.

Dusk was settling on the city. The streetlights were not yet lit, but soft light shone from many windows. A latticework of penumbras was woven between the illuminations and the encroaching darkness, and Waggoner had to admit that the effect was not unpleasing. It was nothing, however, like sunset in Telluride, when the western sky became inflamed with deep vivid hues and the mountains donned a mantle of fuchsia, mauve, and lavender. "Alpenglow," the German and Austrian miners called it.

Waggoner turned into a side street and followed it for several blocks until he came to a small park. The air in the park was fresher, perceptibly so, and the noise of the city muted by its trees and shrubbery. Waggoner sat on a bench. He was continually amazed by the city's capacity to tire him. In the mountains he rarely felt exhaustion, even after the exertions of hiking. In New York, it weighed on him like excess clothing from the moment he arrived. Of course, he had not been sleeping well. For several months his sleep had been irregular, at best. In fact, if he were to be honest with himself, he had never been a champion sleeper. Not in his adult life, at least. It was a problem, he thought, that traced its way to his early days in Telluride and the fascination that he had quickly developed with its nightlife. He had come from the agrarian timetable of rural Illinois, where one awoke with the dawn and went to bed soon after supper. Life in Telluride, after dark, was renewed. It was as if there were two distinct and disparate identities to the town: The daylight version was all about the hustle and bustle of business and the normal enterprise of life; at night, it was about revelry and license.

It had been Wells who had introduced him to the seductions of the night, and not just the first time that he took him gambling — the night of his uncle's dinner party that had ended with Wells pistol-whipping a tough to unconsciousness. Waggoner had, at first, been shy to further test Telluride's nighttime offerings. He had even, on several occasions, turned down Wells' invitations. It did not seem to him that carousing was a respectable or even acceptable pastime for an aspiring banker. His Uncle James, he knew, would not approve, and he dared not suggest the possibility to Mary Reade for fear of recrimination. He came to see, however, that gambling and drinking and dancing held little stigma in Telluride. Not in 1896. Indeed, it almost seemed that more opprobrium was attached to not going out on the town at night than the other way around. The town had come a long way, and quickly, from its lawless and exuberant early years, but it had not yet been completely gentrified. When Waggoner arrived, it was still a man's town, and what men did, so long as it did not specifically impinge on the public good, were not matters for public reproach.

Waggoner's second introduction came one night after he had dined alone at the Cosmopolitan Restaurant at the Sheridan Hotel. He was celebrating his third month in town and his progress at the bank. His dinner had been a phenomenon to which he was strictly unaccustomed. A bowl of vichyssoise to start was followed by a selection of seafood and then a pork tenderloin, through which his knife had seemed to slip by dint of its own weight. For dessert, he had had fresh strawberries with fresh whipped cream. If anyone would have suggested even six months earlier that he would eat such a sumptuous meal a mile and a half above sea level, and surrounded by nothing but rugged isolation, he would have laughed out loud.

His waiter, an Italian with superb manners and sporadic control of English, had tried unsuccessfully to entice him with an extensive list of wines, both Californian and European. Waggoner declined, incapable of shedding his provincialism quite that far.

As he was leaving the restaurant, Wells caught sight of him from the Sheridan's bar and was waiting for him on the boardwalk outside. Perhaps it had been the result of his lavish dining, Waggoner wasn't sure, but he found himself unwilling to argue against or resist Wells' insistence that he come into the saloon. The bar at the Sheridan had been imported from Austria and was made of solid cherry. It had a high polish and shone as brilliantly as the brass spittoons that occupied strategic locations around the room. The walls were covered in calfskin and were hung with paintings of voluptuous naked ladies. Wells swept Waggoner through the saloon as if he were welcoming him as a guest into his own home. Past the bar, he parted long velvet drapes that hung in a wide doorway. Stepping through, Waggoner found himself in another room as big as the first, perhaps bigger, that was filled with tables of men playing cards and roulette. A haze of cigar and pipe smoke hung above the tables and seemed to absorb the sound of the men's voices, which, compared to the boisterousness of the saloon, were low and earnest.

"Have you still not played faro?" asked Wells, directing him toward a table on which lay a large cloth-covered board.

"No, never."

"Splendid!" laughed Wells. "Another bout of beginner's luck coming up."

Indeed, Waggoner had been lucky again that night; very lucky. He had many times since wondered what would have happened had he not been so lucky. Or whether winning as much as he had should even have been called good luck. As it was, he won big and basked again, as he had on the first occasion at The Gold Band, in the approbation that came with victory. He had heard of men finding strength in a bottle: for him, it seemed to come with a large pile of chips.

It had been that first night playing faro, a game of pure luck rather than skill, that Waggoner had met Henry Baisch, who owned a pharmacy and jewelry store. Over the years, the two had become close. Though not so rich or influential as Wells, Baisch was comparably urbane and debonair, as comfortable with a French menu or a snifter of brandy as Waggoner was awkward. Baisch always wore a large and ornately crafted gold ring that was set with a four-carat diamond. The diamond flashed with prismatic effect when Henry dealt cards or toyed absently with a stack of chips. In his store, by a process not dissimilar to the mortar and pestle technique by which he prepared medications, Baisch was able to create a pulp of yellowish concentrate out of high-grade ore brought to him by the miners. Using a weak solution of deadly poisonous potassium or sodium cyanide, fine particles of gold and silver would be dissolved out of the pulp. Henry would either charge the miners for his processing work or buy the resulting product. The high-grade had been, as a rule, stolen and hidden in double brow hats or in canvas tubes stitched inside the miners' pant legs.

It had been a disgruntled high-grader, it was believed, who, dissatisfied with the price he had been paid for his purloined ore, had shot and killed Baisch in 1921. Waggoner recalled with unsettling clarity the sudden and complete nausea he had experienced, as if he had been punched hard in the stomach, when he saw the headline in the *Journal* the morning after the murder: "Lone Man Holds up H.C. Baisch and E.M. Arthur, Shoots Baisch in Cold Blood." The newspaper had termed the killing "the most diabolical in the history of the city or county." In addition to Arthur, who had been standing with Baisch conversing under an arc light at the corner of Colorado and Aspen, there had been another eyewitness to the crime. Ida Foster, proprietress of the Quality Hat Store next door to Ekhelm's Tailor Shop, saw a masked man step out from the side of the tailor's and approach the two men with a drawn gun. Mrs. Foster saw Baisch hand over a few dollars taken from his pocket, as much as he ever carried on his person, and then the gunman tried to snatch the diamond ring from his finger. In the struggle that ensued, the gun went off, firing its deadly load into Baisch's gut. The robber turned and fled.

Baisch had been extremely popular and respected, notwithstanding his recognized role as a fence for high-graders, and his interment at the Lone Tree Cemetery had been attended by better than half the town.

Too often, Waggoner ruminated, the town had been brought together by grief over the loss of friends and loved ones. Most heavily beset were the companions and families of miners. It seemed that there was no end to the list of ways that a miner could meet his end. Cave-ins, premature explosions of dynamite, falling down shafts, being crushed by buckets of ore or large slabs of rock, electrocution, poisoning by mercury used for processing, being blown up by a candle dropped in a box of detonators — each and all of these were all too common types of fatality. Alcohol, which contributed to brawling, shootings, and muggings, and which exacerbated the effects of consumption brought on by constant work in cold, damp conditions with no ventilation, was another frequent agent. With the introduction of power drills — "widow-makers" they were called — men's lungs were further tortured by the constant intake of quartz dust. Suicide was common. Prostitutes, too, were frequent suicide victims, though their deaths were not honored by the long funeral corteges of the miners, and no words of commendation or sorrow were engraved for them on Lone Tree tombstones. Venereal disease and suicide were the most common causes of their deaths. Many died, as well, due to complications from abortion and drug addiction. Murder by jealous johns and rival whores was not infrequent.

Waggoner pulled the folded telegram from his jacket pocket and opened it. The light was inadequate for him to re-read the few words from his friend, but it didn't matter — he saw them clearly in his mind. He was not surprised that Anise had been convicted. He had expected it. Still, it was not easy to accept that it had actually occurred, that she was truly going to prison. Waggoner hung his head. The effect on him of Harry Miller's words was disproportionate to their number.

⚜ ⚜ ⚜

The Wall Street branch of the Chase National Bank was an imposing structure, with grand fluted columns and granite block on the outside and polished walnut paneling and marble on the inside. There were leather armchairs and thick, richly colored carpets that leant an air of a gentlemen's club. Whether the soaring atrium of the lobby simply dissipated voices and noise or everyone was deliberately, self-consciously, quiet, Waggoner couldn't tell. Either way, there was a sepulchral hush to the place that did nothing to allay his nervousness. He would have felt far better amid the hubbub and charivari that he was accustomed to at the Bank of Telluride on Saturday mornings. As it was, walking across the cavernous Chase lobby, his footsteps sounded to him like frightened cries of warning, every smile turned his way a silent interrogation. It was cool in the bank compared to the sticky heat that was already starting to cloy the outside air, yet Waggoner felt flushed and enervated. A trickle of sweat rolled down his ribs and he resisted the urge to loosen his collar and tie.

He approached a woman seated at a heavy desk on which there was an orderly array of paperwork. Her nameplate identified her as Mrs. P. Brubaker. She was exceptionally well turned out, and Waggoner wondered if Mr. Brubaker was a prosperous man, or if New York receptionists were simply far more highly compensated than he was used to.

As calmly as he could, Waggoner handed her his card and explained his business. He was acutely aware that his voice trembled and his hand shook, but the receptionist seemed not to notice. She asked him if he would mind waiting a moment and gestured to one of the leather armchairs. Then she got up and walked to an office near the teller counter, knocked on the door, and disappeared inside. She was gone only briefly but, to Waggoner, it seemed an hour. Sweat continued to run from his underarms, and his shirt was becoming quite damp with it. To distract his thoughts, he surveyed the lobby activity. Among the dozen or so customers coming and going, he noticed a tough-looking character in a poorly tailored suit, too tight, who seemed to have no actual business to conduct, and who was paid no attention by the front door guard or by any of the bank staff. Waggoner realized that the man must be a plainclothes guard. He had heard that many of the big banks were using them to help foil a rising wave of armed robbery. His throat parched at the thought that this man, unlike the guard, was essentially a hired killer.

Mrs. Brubaker emerged from the office and came toward him, her smile flashing as prettily as her expensive jewelry. Behind her was a young man with a high, thin hairline and an earnest set to an otherwise fragile-looking jaw. Mrs. Brubaker introduced him as the officer on duty, and Waggoner immediately forgot his name. It had been an eastern-sounding name — Winslow or Hopkins, perhaps. The young man put out his hand and Waggoner took it. It felt cool and dry, in sharp contrast to his own.

"So, Mr. Waggoner, how may we help you?"

Something in the fellow's tone of voice, or perhaps it was the clear, uncomplicated look of him, his thin receding hair, his insignificant jaw, suddenly put Waggoner at ease. He knew, as soon as the question was posed, that everything was going to go as planned.

"I believe that five hundred thousand dollars was credited to my bank's account here yesterday," he answered.

"I see. And what was the nature of the credit?" The young banker seemed pleased, proud to be dealing with a bank president and a large sum. Waggoner imagined that his Saturday duties ran toward more prosaic affairs: helping a widow reconcile her account or understand how a check she didn't remember writing had been cleared through her account, or listening to the complaints of a young couple over the fees the bank charged for its services.

"There would have been several wires, instructions from Chase Manhattan's correspondent banks in Denver, to transfer funds from their accounts with Chase to the Bank of Telluride's account at this branch."

"I see. Well, that should be no problem to verify. Will you excuse me a moment?"

He was back a few minutes later. With him he had a file labeled "Bank of Telluride."

"Yes, indeed, Mr. Waggoner. The funds have all been credited to your bank's account."

"I wonder, then," said Waggoner, "if you would be so kind as to certify these drafts?"

He reached into his satchel and produced the drafts that Clarence Downtain had signed and that he himself had filled in with amounts.

The young man took the drafts and examined them. They were all drawn against Chase National and were, in effect, demands for payment. Once certified by him, or another authorized agent of his bank, the drafts became as good as cash. Perhaps better, he thought to himself: Times were turning desperate. Just that morning, he had read in the *The Sun* of a counterfeit operation that had been uncovered by the FBI in Newark. The reporter, Nick Alexander, quoted the agent in charge as estimating that over a million dollars, fake dollars, had been printed and circulated by the counterfeit ring. He had even exhorted the tellers before he opened the bank's doors at nine o'clock to examine the notes presented by customers with special care. No such vigilance was necessary with a properly executed bank draft — especially not one presented in person by a bank president.

"Thank you, Mr. Waggoner," he said, handing back the drafts. "If you would be so kind as to endorse these with your signature, I will verify it and Mr. Downtain's, and then stamp them with Chase National's certification."

"How're things in Telluride?" queried the younger man as Waggoner hurriedly scribbled his name on each draft. "That's a mining town, isn't it?"

"Used to be, yes," answered Waggoner. "Not many mines operating now, though. We're in tight times, I'm afraid." He wanted to tell the obliging young fellow that it was his employer, Chase National, and a syndicate of other New York banks, that had sounded the death knell for his town by refusing to renegotiate a number of critical loans to the last few big mines. He longed to explain to the naïve, eager dupe before him that the New York banks, through short-sighted ignorance and heedless arrogance, had been instrumental in bringing the most beautiful and dynamic town in the country to the brink of collapse. Instead, he smiled wryly and assured the young man that he was quite confident that things would soon take a turn for the better.

"Capital," said the other, taking back the drafts and perfunctorily checking the signatures against those in his file.

"All appears to be in order, Mr. Waggoner. Is there anything else that you require?"

"Yes," said Waggoner. "I need to use these drafts to retire some outstanding loans and to effect some transfers."

"Of course," smiled the Chase banker. For the next several minutes, he noted the details of Waggoner's requests and busily completed the forms and paperwork they necessitated. When he had finished, Waggoner thanked him for his good service.

"Not at all," he demurred. "I wish all the bank's business could be as straightforward."

He pushed back his chair and stood up as Waggoner did, shaking his hand firmly. Then he watched with a satisfied smile as the diminutive Coloradoan walked away across the lobby. Regardless of the fact that everything that he had just done for Waggoner was, as far as he could possibly have known, bona fide and proper, it would cost him his job and irreparably damage his career. In the pitched battle that was soon to be waged over the money that he had just dispatched, the young Chase banker was an early casualty.

CHAPTER EIGHT

From New York, Waggoner headed west again. He took a train to Chicago and then another to Denver and a third to Salt Lake. He slept and read and daydreamed while watching the changing view of countrysides, towns, and cities. At each stop along the way he bought a newspaper: a New York paper, if it was available. His only moments of anxiousness came as he scanned the headlines to see if his name was printed in bold among them. He didn't expect to see it; not yet. He assumed that no one would be the wiser until at least Tuesday, and then, if it broke at all, he imagined the story would be reported late in the week at the earliest. There was even a chance that the story would simply never be printed. It could be that the banks, owing to the unseemly stories already mounting in the papers about their reckless speculation and the losses ensuing from them, would choose to keep the story under wraps. It didn't mean that he could afford to be heedless of apprehension. Whether the news was printed or not, he would be sought. It did mean, though, that he would need to take less precaution, cover his tracks less assiduously.

It seemed to Waggoner, as he moved steadily westward, that years of strain and worry were being left behind with every passing mile. He was on the run, but he felt, ironically, as though he was coming out of hiding for the first time in many years. The truth was that he had never felt like a banker. He had always felt that he was pretending to be something that he wasn't: that he was playing a role that didn't suit him and that he might be exposed at any time as an imposter. He had known from the start, had felt it in his soul, that he could never be like his uncle. He knew when he was given charge of the bank that he could not manage it with anything of his uncle's authority or skill. It was a secret knowledge, and there was literally no one to whom he had ever felt he could confide it. He had not even really wanted the president's job. The thought of it had badly frightened him from the first. Once he had it, his discomfort still remained. If he could have, he would have turned it down, thrown his fate to the wind and hoped that he could find a career that made him feel good about himself, something that allowed him to sleep peacefully at night and hold his head high in the day.

But he couldn't turn it down. It was the expectation of everyone to whom he was most closely connected to accept the prize, the rare and coveted prize of the bank presidency. How could he say no? How could he refuse such an offering when it came with such expectation? He chided himself angrily for his ambivalence, walked endless miles in the mountains trying to clear his head of his fretful notions, steeling himself to do the right thing and to be happy with the privilege conferred on him. He told himself over and over that he merely needed to heed his uncle's training, abide by the black and white rules to which his uncle subscribed. However many times he managed to convince himself of the simplicty of such a course, he as many times failed to find and follow it.

In the early days it didn't seem to matter if his uncle's taut standards slackened. The town was so flush with money that losses by the bank were quickly and easily made up. For every deal that went awry, ten more profitable ones were ready to be made. Then the First National Bank closed its doors, its absentee owners happy to take their gains and be gone and unwilling to any longer devote the care and energy that participating actively in a crap shoot market required. The Bank of Telluride was then the sole bank in town, and Waggoner's days came to seem not unlike a miner's — long and hard — but instead of tunneling through bedrock, buried in the heart of a mountain, he chiseled his way through paper mountains, his desk buried by files and letters, documents and reports. There was too much for him to do. Even with help, and good help was hard to come by, he was forced to work all hours. There were not many trained bankers knocking at his door for a job and, even if there had been, so much of the bank's business depended heavily on knowing the community and understanding mining as well as the hectic and diverse economy that grew from it. The years of his uncle's constant tutelage had taught Waggoner far more than he would ever have the time to pass on. And, too, people didn't want to be fobbed off to an underling. They wanted him. They wanted him to consider and assess their requests and him to get back to them personally. He felt compelled to cut corners, to do what was expeditious rather than what was strictly right or proper.

Then unexpectedly one night, playing cards, his mind more on the things he had left undone on his desk than on what he was holding in his hand, he had been introduced to a stranger by the name of Will Scanlon. Scanlon was brash and bright. And he seemed interested in Waggoner's business, peppering him with questions, while he also managed to win at poker with maddening regularity. He had no banking experience, but he was an accountant and he had worked for a stockbroking house back East. He understood business and finance. He told Waggoner that he liked Telluride and could see making it his home.

"It's a tough town," Waggoner's friend, Harry Miller, warned Scanlon from across the table. "Sometimes we haven't got too much in the way of law here, so chances are better than in most places that you might end up dead or wishing you were after an argument. Winters are bad and the summers short. Everything's twice as expensive as anywhere else, because it's hard to freight it here and because there's nowhere else to buy it. People work hard and are paid poorly. As a rule, the miners hate the mine owners, the Swedes and Finns hate the Poles, who hate the Germans, who hate the Italians, and everybody hates the Mexicans. Between avalanches, floods, rock slides, and bullets, stray or aimed, there's a lot of ways to meet your Maker here."

Scanlon smiled. "Sounds fine to me," he said, and then, turning back to Waggoner, "Have you got an opening?"

Waggoner hired him, warning him that his training would be catch-as-catch-can and that he would probably have to run before he walked.

Two weeks later, he received a letter from a banker in Denver by the name of Charles Downtain. Downtain's in-laws lived in Montrose, he wrote, and he was looking for work in the area. He was not a lender, but he had several years' experience on the deposit side of banking and of managing the day-to-day brass tacks of banking business: effecting transfers; issuing drafts; getting deeds recorded; shipping cash and coin; preparing customer statements; and reconciling the bank's various ledger accounts. These were all matters that Waggoner had managed with help from a revolving circle of staff, none of whom were fully experienced or competent. It was an area that the bank's board of directors specifically fretted about, but Waggoner hadn't the time to devote to it that it needed. Bank operations were generally expense areas, parts of the business that brought in no revenues. He felt it was his responsibility to involve himself as much as he could in making loans, generating interest and fee income, so that expenses, managed or not, could be covered. And, given the demand, he felt little choice.

Within a few days of each other, Downtain and Scanlon joined the bank. Even with the added burden of their salaries, the bank's profits soared. Downtain was a precise and exacting type who watched over the bank's operations and expenses with hard-eyed scrutiny. Scanlon had none of Downtain's humorless preoccupation with details: He was glib to the point of being flippant, and he seemed to delight in making deals. He had a saleman's gregarious character and knew instinctively how to get a customer to warm to him. Many people still preferred to have Waggoner personally involved in all their business, but more and more people seemed not only happy to have Scanlon, but to expect him. He was prompt in coming back with an answer, and he seemed devoted to finding ways to make things work. He said "no" even less often than Waggoner did, but it was through no fear or insecurity or because he was overwhelmed. He simply didn't like to turn loan requests down, assuming that there was always a way to make a deal work. He even delighted in the weaker, more risky transactions, arguing their merits to Waggoner and, when necessary, to the bank's board of directors, with the vigor of a stumping politician. Often the merits centered on the exhorbitant rates and high fees that he could charge on doubtful deals — deals that no one else, no other bank, would have considered feasible.

Waggoner found his life returning to a more civilized pace. He was no longer the first into the bank every morning and the last to leave at night. Increasingly, he was content to let Downtain and Scanlon shoulder much of the work and take on added responsibility. He was no longer distracted when playing cards by thoughts of pending requests and delinquent borrowers. He resumed his customary forays into the mountains and had more time to play with his son at home.

Harry Miller, though delighted to see his friend calmer and more collected than he had been for so long, warned Waggoner not to loosen his grip too far. Not only as a friend but as a shareholder in the bank, he cautioned him especially about Scanlon.

"There are deals that should be done," he said, "and those that shouldn't. Simple as that. Silk purse, sow's ear. Mr. Scanlon has a problem seeing the long view, if you ask me. He's thinking about today and tomorrow and how much money he can wrangle someone into paying as if he were out to break records. He's not thinking about six months or a year or three years. He's not thinking about the loan repaying or paying off, only getting it booked to the ledger and collecting a fat fee."

"He is an accountant, Harry," Waggoner protested. "He understands numbers. Financial numbers. He's not just some rodeo cowboy looking for short thrills."

"Accountants!" snorted Miller. "The best way I can sum up that breed is by a story I heard. Seems as if a shopkeeper needed to hire an assistant. Puts an ad in the paper. First day, a woman comes in to see him, a teacher. 'I have just one question,' says the shopkeep. "How much is two and two?" The teacher answers, 'Two plus two equals four.' 'Very fine,' says the shopkeep. 'I'll be in touch.' Next day, comes an engineer. Same question: how much is two and two? The engineer sets about scribbling equations on a piece of paper and then says: 'Two and two is precisely between 3.86 and 4.14.' 'Very fine,' says the keep. 'I'll be in touch.' Third day, an accountant comes in. He listens to the question, the same question the other two got. Then he looks at the shopkeep, squints a little, looks around the room, goes over to the window, and draws the curtains. He comes back close up to the keep and says in a whisper, 'How much do you want it to be?'"

Waggoner laughed at the story but scoffed anew at Miller's insinuation. Still, he never forgot the joke, and he found that everytime he thought of it, he pictured Will Scanlon as the accountant applying for the job.

It wasn't so much a case of Waggoner ceding responsibilty and authority to Scanlon, it was more one of Scanlon simply taking it. His audacity was extreme, but he was persuasive to the point of being coercive. It had been Scanlon who had talked Waggoner into putting a picture of a beautiful girl on the cover of the bank's annual report to its shareholders and using the picture in its ads. It was Scanlon, too, who dreamed up the idea for a publicity photo showing Waggoner and him behind the bank's teller counter with stacks of shining gold and silver coins, fifty thousand dollars' worth, and a brace of Colt .45s.

"It shows the bank as strong," he argued when Waggoner had at first turned the idea down. "It tells people we have all the money they need and the security to hold the money they don't. T'hell with advertisements about our capital position, our history, our promises. Nobody reads them. If they do, they don't pay attention. Show them a picture of fifty grand of loot stacked like a ransom and a pair of peacemakers, and they know they have nothing to worry about."

This was at a time when people were beginning to worry. The mines were no longer running twenty-four hours a day. Some mines had even closed, and almost all were feeling a pinch. Depositors who had never before concerned themselves with the bank's financial condition now stopped Waggoner on the street or came up to him at the gambling table or after church and asked him, casually, but with concern they couldn't hide, how the bank was doing. It was a time, as well, when Scanlon began to introduce some accounting techniques that Waggoner doubted he would find in any textbook. It was also a time when Waggoner's general good luck at the card table seemed to dry up and disappear like a spring melt stream.

One of the advantages to gambling over other vices, Waggoner had always considered, was that you stood as good a chance of winning as losing. Over time it was, in that sense, more or less a break-even proposition. So long as you played conservatively, knew when to hold or fold, you could change the odds to your favor. Luck was clearly a factor, and not an inconsiderable one. Luck could prevail over rashness and greed, at least in the short term. Waggoner's luck had not always been good, but it had been even. It had been enough. Even if he had experienced a short stretch of bad luck, good luck always came back. And then he landed in a stretch that didn't end. When he became aware that he was being dealt difficult cards and drawing worse ones, time and again, night after night, he reacted first by lightening his bets and throwing his cards in early. That served to reduce his losses, but it didn't stop them. Then he resorted to large bets on bluff hands, but loss of luck is not a private matter with men who gamble regularly and with each other. His bluffs were called. His losses grew.

He changed games, playing dice and roulette instead of cards, but — as his change in poker tactics had — it proved unhelpful. He considered giving up gambling and tried to divert himself with longer walks, more reading, more sleep. It was no use. The thought preyed on him that the only way to make up his losses was to win them back. He felt himself on edge and empty, his patience wearing thin easily. He lost his concentration. He missed his friends and the feel of cards in his hand, the sound of the roulette ball as it ricocheted and of the dice as they were shaken and thrown.

He went back to poker. He hoped that his absence from the tables might have assuaged whatever force accounted for luck or, if there was no such force, that he had bided time enough for balance to tilt again his way. It did not. He won a share of games, but it was by dint only of extra caginess, of playing his hands as astutely as he possibly could. He took satisfaction in becoming the best player he could be, but he still left more money on the table than he took away. The flood that his losses had been turned into a stream and then a trickle, but he was never able to staunch it completely. And the occasional ruptures were not offset by jackpot wins. For the first time since he had placed a chip at roulette with Bulkeley Wells in the back room of The Gold Band, Waggoner found that he had to subsidize his gambling with monies that were needed for other things. And still he played on, confident that it was just a matter of more time, of allowing the continuum of winning and losing to modulate back to his favor. He found himself needing to manage his money as cleverly and sharply as he now had to manage his poker hands. He put off purchases that weren't esssential, began paying bills more slowly, and borrowed money from other banks, other bankers. He took out loans to repay loans. The house that he owned free and clear he mortgaged and borrowed more.

Just as he struggled alone with the secret of his unhappiness as a banker, he revealed nothing of his financial worries to anyone. He began frequenting altering gaming establishments, gambling with a mix of different groups to keep anyone from witnessing the consistency of his losses. He opened accounts in his name only so that his wife was not privy to the flow of funds that passed through them. He reimbursed himself from the funds for expenses that were not to do with household business. Instead of his customary five dollar contribution to the church's collection basket each Sunday, he placed a single dollar bill. When his clothes became worn, threadbare, weakened at the seams or the knees and elbows, he asked Mary to sew or patch them rather than throw them away and buy new ones, happy to let her and others consider that he simply didn't care about appearances, or that he had an eccentric and growing predilection for the comfort of old familiar attire.

Now, all of that was behind him. What lay ahead, he wasn't at all sure. Very possibly it was nothing good. Things would go well and work out, or they wouldn't, but they would never be the same as they had been, and that was perfectly acceptable to him. It saddened him that he had been unable to bid proper goodbyes to his friends, that he hadn't even been able to arrange with his wife the exact time or place or circumstances of their return to each other. He took comfort in the sure knowledge that she loved him. In that, through better than a quarter of a century, she had been unfaltering. When she had seen him off at the train station in Olathe, knowing nothing concretely of the particulars of his urgent and solitary visit to New York, she had hugged him tightly and whispered words that told him she would never forsake him in body or in spirit. As his train pulled away, she stood waving and didn't move before he lost sight of her.

CHAPTER NINE

September 6 — Telluride

Alta Cassietto was in her office late, anxiously preparing for the next day's issue of the *Journal*. The week before, there had been two announcements in the paper that helped explain her fervor. One had advised that the paper was no longer the *Daily Journal* but the *Telluride Journal*, a weekly. As it had been stated in the editorial:

> The management has tried its best to keep the paper's head above water, but mining conditions in this district have become such in the last two years that there is no further excuse for the printing of a daily newspaper as mines shut down and activities in that line are hopelessly in the dumps.

The other announcement was that those editorial words were the last to be read from Claude H. Trickett. The job of editor and manager was being turned over to Alta.

Alta had learned of her promotion only the day before it came out in the paper, and it had still not quite registered in her mind. Throughout the week, she had found herself stealing glances at the new nameplate on her desk and shaking her head as if she couldn't actually credit what it said: Alta Cassietto — Editor. There was no mistaking the extra work, however, on publication night.

Frank McNamara was working late with her, preparing advertising copy and job work. McNamara was the entire mechanical department of the newspaper, and Alta felt blessed to have the benefit of his long experience and cheerful disposition. Without either one, she was sure she would have run screaming into the night long before this. It was only a small paper, four pages, but, between headline stories wired in from the United Press, council business, legal notices, local news stories, and her popular "People You Know" segment, there seemed to be ten pages of content to arrange and fit and edit. It reminded Alta of a difficult jigsaw puzzle pieced together without a picture to go by. She wished that the Carrington Chevrolet Company of Montrose had not quite so many models to list in their ad. It was hard for her to believe that one automobile manufacturer could have eleven different models to sell, but there they all were, in black and white, with their varying prices: the Coach — $595; the Roadster — $525; the Phaeton — $525; the Coupe — $595; the Sport Coupe — $645; the Sedan — $675; and so on. Then there were the cigarette ads, both Lucky and Chesterfield. The Lucky ad had a lengthy quote by H.U.D. Seagrave, the automobile racer, who had broken the world's land speed record in March, when he drove 231 miles per hour at Daytona.

"I want to keep trim and fit," Seagrave was quoted. "I want to feel the glow of pep and health at all times. The thought of excess weight really frightens me. I welcome a Lucky instead of sweets and things that would make me soft."

The Chesterfield ad showed a beautiful girl of about Alta's age completing a graceful, reaching, backhanded tennis swing. The copy read: "...on the court, it's FLASH...in a cigarette, it's TASTE."

Alta sniffed impatiently at all three ads that together took up the better part of half a page. It was space that she would have preferred to fill with news or human-interest stories, but she quickly reminded herself how fortunate she was to have any big advertisers left. If it was up to local businesses with their small box ads — Elskamp Brothers Market, Perino's Store, Long's Men's Wear, the Segerburg Theatre (currently showing Wolf Song with Gary Cooper and Lupe Velez, the latter billed as "exotic daughter of Old Mexico") — she wouldn't have half the revenue she needed to support the paper's operation. Or to keep the price at five cents, which she knew was as much as she could expect to charge and still maintain circulation. Even the Bank of Telluride had cut back on its layout and copy and was now using a simple box ad.

Alta looked back through the United Press releases. She chose a report about the landing of the German dirigible, Zephyr, at Lakehurst, New Jersey, after completing the first commercial circumnavigation of the world. She whistled at the pace the zeppelin had maintained, accomplishing its feat in just over twenty-one days.

Frank McNamara stopped what he was doing and Alta read him the story. He shook his head skeptically.

"You wouldn't catch me floatin' 'round in that oversized gas balloon," he snorted. "I'd rather ride the Liberty Bell tram down-mountain in the dark. Damn people must be crazy as loons." Muttering, he turned back to his work.

Alta clucked in agreement, but, in fact, thought that she would very much like to ride on the Zephyr and be cheered to a landing by ten thousand spectators, which the UP article reported had gathered to watch the historic touchdown.

There was a story from Wall Street, but she decided that the drastic fall in stock prices earlier in the month that had been precipitated by an unexpected rise in interest rates had received enough coverage. There was a short piece out of Washington that told of President Hoover's yacht being taken out of commission, thus saving taxpayers three hundred thousand dollars a year and freeing 148 sailors to be assigned to naval vessels. There was news from Chicago, "blood-splotched Chicago," as the reporter labeled the city, about a further flare up in the so-called "Beer War" being waged by the "Bugs" Moran Irish gang against an Italian one. The Russians and Chinese were skirmishing on the Manchurian border, a rebellion was still being fought against federal troops in Sonoma, Mexico, and, closer to home, a story had come in that morning from a local source about a bootleg raid in Ouray by federal agents. Roy Clark and "Kid" West, ringleaders of the outlaws, had escaped, but there had been several arrests and bail had been set at fifteen hundred dollars apiece. It was the sort of story, Alta decided, that a local newspaper was simply compelled to put on its front page. It was the sort of story, too, that would boost sales by a few good nickels, she was sure.

She was just starting to tell Frank her choices for the front page and how she saw them arranged and set, when the phone rang. Frank held up his hand for her to hold her thought and lifted the phone's receiver.

"Yes, Betty," he said to the town's operator. "She's here." He was silent, listening. "I see. Well, hold just a minute.

"Someone calling from Denver," he said, the receiver pressed against his shoulder. "Betty says he sounds kind of jumpy. She says she figures him for a newspaper man because he wasn't very polite."

Alta smiled and tried to imagine who could be calling her from Denver at such a late hour. She stepped to the phone.

"Hello?"

"Alta Cassietto?"

"Yes."

"This is Ray Stroud, Alta. I'm a reporter."

"Yes, I know your name. I've read your pieces in the Post. What can I do for you, Mr. Stroud?" She made a quizzical gesture at Frank.

"It's not so much about doing something for me," answered Stroud. "More something I want to do for you."

"Yes?"

"Yes. You see, there's a story breaking here that's going to be big. Very big. And it's all about one of your hometown worthies. I thought you might like a hot lead, might like to see my copy. You're welcome to run it in your paper as a special."

Instinctively, Alta thought of Bulkeley Wells. He had not been heard from since he left town with the platinum blonde daughter of a boarding house owner. He was the first Telluride person to come to her mind that might do something considered newsworthy in Denver.

"Well, thank you very much," she said, a note of uncertainty in her voice. "I was just laying out tomorrow's edition. I'm afraid we've had to cut back to a weekly format, and there's not a lot of room. But, if it's a big story, I'll make it work."

"It's big, alright," confirmed Stroud. "Front page, banner headline big. And that's in New York! I think you're definitely going to want to find room for this."

Alta was beginning to share the operator's opinion of Ray Stroud. "Can you tell me what the story's about, Mr. Stroud?"

"It's about money, ma'am. A lot of it. Half a million bucks. It was withdrawn from six New York banks on, shall we say, questionable authority. It's about a bank job. Slickest little caper I've ever heard of. And the man who pulled it off is one of Telluride's very own."

Alta's mind, racing with thoughts moments prior about how to order the stories for tomorrow's edition, now went blank. She had no idea who Stroud could be talking about. There were one or two unsavory locals who she could imagine might try to rob the Bank of Telluride or its sister bank in Norwood. But half a million dollars from New York banks? She was stumped.

"You still there?"

"Yes, I'm here. Sorry. I was trying to guess who in the world you could mean, but I'm afraid I haven't the least idea."

"Well, I'd be mighty surprised if you did. I don't think this guy qualifies as a usual suspect. But, then again, these days, who knows? I'm afraid the story's going to cause some ruckus in your town, Alta. It's a heck of a heist, but it's going to be an even bigger scandal. Turns out the bank robber is also a banker. His name's C.D. Waggoner."

If Stroud had just said that it was Herbert Hoover who had stolen the money, Alta couldn't have been more stunned. Immediately, the enormity of the implications flashed through her mind. Whatever precarious balance Telluride was managing to strike between living and dying, past and future, she knew the scale had just been tipped firmly in the wrong direction.

She had been standing by Frank's desk, but now she slumped against it.

"Please wire your story to us, Mr. Stroud," she spoke into the phone. "We will be much obliged. Thank you."

"You're welcome," answered Stroud. "I wish it were better news. I hope not too much hardship comes from it."

Alta hung the receiver in its cradle as if it were fragile enough to shatter.

"What is it?" asked Frank. "Bad news?"

She nodded silently. Then, after a few moments during which the wire service machine began to tap out the story coming from Denver, she said, "Better roll up your sleeves, Frank. Looks as if it's going to be a little longer of an evening than we had thought."

🐝 🐝 🐝

Ray Stroud got his scoop directly from Grant McFerson. Stroud often wrote about financial affairs, and he had more than once had complimentary things to say about the state's banking commissioner. He thought McFerson had a devilish job: Banks were stretched thin all across Colorado. In addition to defaults brought on by the dismal economic conditions, banks had been further beset of late by a rash of fraud. McFerson and his people were being run just about ragged. What they weren't shutting down, they were desperately trying to shore up. Even the strongest banks were not entirely immune to the plague of foreclosures and charged-off loans that was infesting the state. And the criminal aspects were significant. For over a year, McFerson and his examiners had been working through a two million dollar embezzlement case involving one of Denver's top banks.

Stroud had received a call from McFerson on Tuesday. The commissioner asked him if he would like to join him for a working lunch. The reporter happily accepted.

Stroud had visited McFerson's office before and his impression this time, as then, was of a military command post. There were maps and charts spread over the walls and boxes of files stacked on the floor.

McFerson's staff came and went from his office with a quiet urgency. There was no frivolity. To a person, they seemed determined and disciplined, and no one more so than McFerson, himself. He was tall with clean, chiseled features and a clear intense gaze. He was perhaps ten years Stroud's senior, which showed in the gray at his temples and in the wrinkles at the corners of his eyes, but nowhere else. He certainly looked the part of a future governor, a heavily rumored possibility, but there was little of the politician in his character, Stroud thought. He was quiet, self-effacing, and candid. He was a "stand-up guy," as Stroud's wisecracking junior colleagues would say, and that seemed basis enough to disqualify him from politics.

McFerson waited as two of his subalterns finished rummaging through a box of files. Finding what they were looking for, they left, and McFerson closed his office door. Stroud had not expected much small talk, and he wasn't disappointed. McFerson took a folded piece of paper from the top of one of the piles on his desk and handed it to the newspaperman without a word. Stroud unfolded it. It was a letter written by hand. The paper was from the Mansfield Hotel in New York. The writing was small and looked as if it had been hastily scrawled. The date at the top was August 29. There was no heading, other than the hotel's, and it was addressed to McFerson.

> *Dear Mr. McFerson, I have just received a gift of five hundred thousand dollars from the Denver Clearing House. At least, I presume it was a gift, for there were no strings attached to it. I am using the money to square some matters for my bank and to help rescue my depositors from losses that they do not deserve to suffer. You will no doubt become involved in this matter, and I am sure I can count on you to defend the interests of the little people against the conscienceless Denver and New York banks. They are rapacious and soulless, and nothing would delight me more than to be a part of their downfall. It seems to me that there is no longer any honor in my profession, nor any courtesy or manners. Bankers are no longer gentlemen looking out for the interests of their communities, but immoral predators in relentless pursuit of profit.*

The next two lines were difficult to make out. Stroud scanned the rest of the page, which was rambling and less than coherent, as best he could tell. The signature at the bottom was illegible except for the initials, C.D.

He looked questioningly at McFerson.

"It came last week," said the commissioner. "It's from C.D. Waggoner, president of the Bank of Telluride. At the time, we were aware of nothing amiss, and my assumption, frankly, was that the man was drunk or mentally troubled, or both. I phoned a lawyer friend of mine — you probably know him, Elwood Rabenold — who's also a friend of Waggoner's and handles much of the bank's legal work. He agreed that it seemed Waggoner was suffering some form of disorder. Then things started to get pretty stirred up."

"Stirred up?"

"Yes, sir. Very. I got a call last Thursday from Ed Bremmer at the International Trust Company. He said his correspondent bank in New York, the Equitable Trust Company, had just sent him an overdraft notice for seventy-five thousand dollars. I assumed he had some sort of short-term funding mismatch and was calling to let me know that his bank would be requesting an overnight loan. Instead, he told me that the reason for the overdraft was a fraud."

Stroud whistled. "A seventy-five thousand dollar bunco, eh? Not bad. What's the connection to Waggoner and the half million?"

"The connection," said McFerson, "appears to be direct and complete. On Friday, we heard the same story from five other Denver banks and their New York correspondents. Each of the New York banks had received nearly identical instructions from their Denver correspondents, authorizing funds to be credited to the account of the Bank of Telluride at Chase Manhattan's Wall Street branch. Two of the banks were instructed to credit one hundred thousand each, and the other four, seventy-five thousand each."

"That's half a million, alright," said Stroud. "And they all acted on the instructions?"

"They had no reason not to. The telegrams were coded properly, and it hasn't been uncommon over the years for there to be quite large transfers to the Bank of Telluride's accounts. Taken individually, the requests wouldn't have raised an eyebrow."

"So what happened to the money? Did New York get wind of what was up in time to save their funds?"

"Afraid not. It appears that the very morning, a week ago Saturday, that the funds were credited to Chase Manhattan,

Waggoner himself came to their Wall Street branch with a number of Bank of Telluride drafts. They were all signed by the bank's cashier. Waggoner presented his credentials at the Chase branch as cool as can be, endorsed the drafts, and had them certified. Then he used the drafts to pay a number of debts. He paid off a one hundred thousand dollar note of the Bank of Telluride's to the Central Hanover and Trust Company and another for a hundred thousand owed by a Telluride meat packing company that I believe Waggoner owns or controls. He paid off a seventy thousand dollar personal note. A fourth draft of one hundred ninety-five thousand was placed in another New York bank for credit to the First National Bank of Pueblo and further credit to the Bank of Telluride. And a fifth draft for thirty thousand dollars was similarly placed to the credit of the Telluride bank's account with the Continental Bank of Salt Lake City."

"One hundred thousand paid off the Bank of Telluride debt," said Stroud, making notes. "Another one hundred thousand paid off the packing company's loan. Then, seventy thousand to his personal debt and thirty thousand to the Salt Lake bank — that makes three hundred thousand — and one hundred ninety-five thousand to Pueblo. That's four hundred ninety-five thousand in all — five thousand dollars unaccounted for."

"Quite," said McFerson. "Five thousand never left the Chase Manhattan account. I don't know if he left it there deliberately to somehow obfuscate his larceny, or if he simply panicked and fled without it."

"Frankly," offered Stroud, "by the sound of it, it doesn't seem as if he were terribly panicky, does it?"

"No," agreed McFerson, "it doesn't. Have you ever met him?"

"Can't say that I have. At least, I don't recall."

"It wouldn't be too surprising if you didn't recall. He's a nondescript, little man and possibly the last person in the world you would expect to pull a brazen con like this. I honestly have to suspect his sanity."

Stroud nodded but said nothing. If Waggoner was crazy, it seemed the fox's variety to him. Half a million dollars had just been spirited away from the banks it belonged to by virtual sleight of hand, and the prestidigitator had disappeared with a good lead. Stroud smiled inwardly. This had the making of a good story, to say the least. Little Telluride was about to grow very big on the national map.

🎇 🎇 🎇

After Ray Stroud left his office, Grant McFerson wasted little time. He was familiar, too familiar, with the dynamics of bank failures, and the first rule was to act quickly to limit loss. Whether Waggoner had acted to save himself or his depositors, whether he was sane or demented, would fall to others to judge. McFerson had an opinion on both matters, but they weren't germane to his immediate duty. And that was to safeguard the integrity of Colorado's banking system. More specifically, in this case, it was to do whatever he could to somehow insulate the people of Telluride from what could be the dire and long-reaching consequences of the town's only bank collapsing.

He made two telephone calls to set into motion immediate closure of the Bank of Telluride. Then he phoned the state attorney general to apprise him of a suit, or a multitude of suits, that would surely be coming. Waggoner's would undoubtedly be a federal case, and all stops would be pulled out to recover the stolen funds for the New York banks. Whether right or wrong in the eyes of the law, McFerson felt it his moral obligation to fight the New York banks on behalf of the Telluride depositors.

"Jesus, Joseph, and Mary," he swore quietly as he waited for someone at the attorney general's office to pick up the ringing telephone. He ran his free hand back and forth over his short-cropped, salt-and-pepper hair. Then, surprising himself, he began to laugh. He was not a great admirer of the big New York banks. They were, in his opinion, fickle speculators with no commitment to any cause other than their own. McFerson was originally from a small Front Range town, and he had cut his teeth in the industry as a community banker. He identified strongly with towns like Telluride, and felt empathy for Waggoner. He could never admit it to a living soul, but he secretly wished that the New York banks would not get a penny back, and that Buck Waggoner would never be caught.

CHAPTER TEN

✧

Alta Cassietto's disbelief grew with every line that came across the wire from Denver. The headline read: "C.D. Waggoner Wanted for Half-Million Bank Swindle." Beneath that, Stroud had written, "Large New York Banks Fall Victim to Clever Hoax for Benefit of Local Bank."

Frank McNamara shook his head sadly. He had lived in Telluride for many years and had witnessed his share of the town's intrigues and escapades. Murders, robberies, feuds, suicides — as a newspaperman, he had known more details over the years than he cared to remember. Telluride had known its share of natural tragedies, as well: Fires, floods, and avalanches had robbed the town of many lives. As he stood beside Alta reading Stroud's article as it was slowly printed, he recognized that Telluride's most sensational story ever was being told. As Alta had, he quickly deduced its tragic angle. The bank was one of Telluride's last remaining bulwarks against the tide of collapse. So long as the bank could continue to support the community with loans and protect people's savings, there was hope for the future. If the bank failed, the town would quickly follow. And if the bank's state of affairs were such that C.D. Waggoner would be pushed to steal, and not just a little, then Frank had no doubt that it would fail.

As Alta read, she could not banish the image in her mind of Waggoner and his wife driving out of town at night just two weeks before. How clearly she saw his face as he had looked up at her window, his wistful smile. She realized now how truly rueful that smile had been.

She had known Waggoner since she had been a little girl, had picked dandelions from his yard and strung them into necklaces. His son Delos had taught her to ride his pony. Like most everyone in town, she had had an account at his bank for many years. She could not possibly count the number of times she had seen him at his desk there, talking to customers or working on papers. There was, perhaps, no one more familiar in town, more recognizable, than Waggoner. With his retiring avuncular manner, he perfectly fit the role of small town banker who had to be confessor, counselor, and confidante, in addition to financier. Alta had no doubt that if a poll was to be taken, the most trusted man in Telluride would be C.D. Waggoner, hands down. Not that he wasn't eccentric. He wore old baggy suits with patches and rambled through the mountains on his own in all kinds of weather. And it was known that he had a fondness for the gambling tables. But he didn't drink, whore, smoke, spit, or swear in a town where those activities often seemed the primary pursuit of the majority of the male population.

Once Stroud's story came all the way through, Frank blocked it out for the front page and set the type. The byline read: "Denver, September 6, Special to the *Telluride Journal*." The article was long and detailed, but Alta decided against any editing, and Frank had to comprehensively rework the layout of the edition that he and Alta had previously agreed on. It took him a long time, and when he was finished, before running the press, he re-read Stroud's article in full.

> C.D. Waggoner, President of the Bank of Telluride, is the object of an international search following the revelation Wednesday of an alleged $500,000 swindle, which authorities characterized as one of the most amazing in banking history. Banking authorities, police, and private detectives put their heads together today in an attempt to locate the dazzling financier who fraudulently negotiated a half million credit and escaped.
>
> Delos Waggoner, son of the bank president and assistant cashier for the institution, who is visiting in Denver, was questioned late yesterday by Grant McFerson, state bank commissioner, and other officials working on the case. He denied having any knowledge of the transaction.
>
> One of the unique phases of the alleged swindle, authorities said, is the fact that after the money had been placed at his disposal in the New York banks, a man representing himself as Waggoner ordered it deposited in other institutions to the credit of the Bank of Telluride.
>
> The scheme to build up the $500,000 credit was manipulated through coded telegrams sent from Denver, it was revealed. Last Friday, six telegrams were sent from Denver, some through the Postal and others through the

Western Union, to the New York banking houses that corresponded with Denver's largest banks.

Each telegram, in the American Bankers Association code, was signed in the name of a Denver banker by typewriter and authorized the correspondent of the Denver banks to deposit money in the Wall Street branch of the Chase National Bank to the credit of Waggoner's bank.

A telegram purporting to be sent by the Denver National Bank authorized the deposit of $100,000. The same amount was apparently authorized by the First National Bank and $75,000 each from the United States National, the Colorado National, the American National, and the International Trust Company.

The six New York banks, acting on the telegrams from Denver, deposited sums aggregating $500,000 with the Chase National Bank.

Saturday, a man representing himself as Waggoner presented drafts of the Telluride bank at the Chase National Bank and asked that they be certified.

The drafts, according to information received here, were properly made out. They were reported to have borne the names of both Waggoner and the bank cashier. Waggoner's name was reported to have been endorsed on the back of the drafts.

Officials of the Chase National Bank, in view of the $500,000 credit to Waggoner, certified the drafts. That same day, it was learned, one of the drafts bearing the certification of the Chase National was presented to the Central Hanover and Trust Company in payment of a note of the Bank of Telluride for $100,000.

Another draft was presented to the Hanover Bank to pay the $100,000 debt of a Telluride packing company. The firm was presumed to be the Norwood Cattle Company.

A third draft was presented to the Hanover Bank in payment of Waggoner's personal indebtedness of $70,000.

A fourth draft of $195,000 was presumed to have been placed in a New York bank to the credit of the First National Bank of Pueblo, for that bank was notified Wednesday that the $195,000 was on deposit for the Pueblo bank for the credit of the Bank of Telluride.

> *A fifth draft for $30,000 similarly was placed to the credit of the Telluride bank with the Continental Bank of Salt Lake City.*
>
> *These drafts account for $495,000 of the $500,000 alleged to have been placed fraudulently to Waggoner's credit with the Chase National. The Chase National Bank still has $5,000 of the $500,000 deposit credited to Waggoner's account.*

McNamara shook his head slowly, then made his final preparations to roll the press.

☙ ☙ ☙

Alta Cassietto had learned early in her newspaper career that the public often cared less for facts than it did for figments. So, she was unsurprised by the position quickly adopted by much of the town that Waggoner was a hero, a modern-day David taking on the Goliath banks of Wall Street. That McFerson's agents had moved in that very morning and were shutting down the bank, even as people were opening the paper and experiencing the shock of the banner headline, would cause them little apparent concern. People read the article as if it were a fictitious literary creation that she had personally concocted. They stopped her eagerly in the street to recommend their preferred outcome.

The two most popularly shared sentiments were that Waggoner had done it to save the town and that he would never be caught. Of course, there were dissenters. Coincidentally or not, they were the ones who had the biggest stakes in the bank, either as depositors or investors. W.B. Van Atta was perhaps the leading spokesman for this contingent. Alta was standing behind him at Perino's grocery when he angrily interrupted a discussion about Waggoner's feat.

"Piffle!" he declaimed. "The blasted fool's either deranged, imbecilic, or the most conniving huckster this town's ever known. Take your pick!"

Van Atta had recently taken over as county treasurer following the Koen scandal. He owned one of the biggest retail businesses in Telluride and was considered a man of prestige and influence. Still, he didn't easily win converts to his side. The town seemed to Alta to be infected with a virulent need to believe two things: that one of their own could not betray their trust; and, regardless of the why or wherefore of Waggoner's actions, no one would actually lose any money.

Alta wanted to believe that Waggoner's act had been a selfless one, even if desperate, and that the matter would, one way or another, be settled in favor of the bank's depositors. She could not convince herself, however, of either proposition. Although she was certainly not sure of all the facts, her reporter's instinct told her that the case for Waggoner's defense could not be a strong one. It would come as no surprise to her if the bank's doors were to remain closed for a long time.

🎖 🎖 🎖

The Cañon City penitentiary was remote and isolated and surrounded by a high barbed fence. It was situated on a small rise, from which sere flat land stretched in all directions, its soil thin and weak, capable of supporting nothing more than clumps of sage and low-growing cacti. In the afternoons, windstorms were common; the swirled clouds of chalky dust they lifted from the land were the only liveliness apparent, apart from the mournful calls of coyotes in the evenings and in the stark hours before dawn.

Anise Koen hated the jail. Not because she couldn't leave it, not because it was cold and inhuman in its design and construction, its policies and procedures. She hated it because it was invariable. Each day was the same as the one before it. Like the landscape, the jail and life inside it were bleak and dull. From the moment she had first entered her cell, a hard, bare cubicle, she had felt her soul begin to parch and wither.

Although the Cañon City facility housed all kinds of criminals, including murderers and arsonists, there were different levels of security. In the women's section, the conditions were not intolerably harsh. Its numbing routine, however, was unrelenting.

There were some fifty women incarcerated with her, and she saw little possibility of becoming friendly with any of them. It wasn't that she was unwilling or incapable; she felt no particular superiority or disdain toward the others. She sensed from them, however, both individually and collectively, a coldness and separation that was as palpable as the steel bars at her window.

There were books and magazines to read, but the books were all from the lowest rung on the literary ladder and the magazines were severely dated, their pages crinkled and torn and often simply missing, so that trying to read the continuation of an article was usually an exercise in frustration. Newspapers were sporadic, at best, and, like the magazines, were stale by a considerable period.

She had heard from Walter Hillman in a letter about C.D. Waggoner's astounding larceny and about the closure of the Telluride bank. It had been as difficult for her to accept the facts of what Hillman wrote as it was to accept those of her own circumstances. By his account, the mild little man who had come to her aid when no one else would was now the object of an international search. She hoped he would never be caught. She hoped he would never come to know the diurnal stultification of life in prison.

Other than short notes that she received almost daily from her mother, Hillman's was the only letter she had received since arriving at Cañon City. He was a good writer, obviously more comfortable putting words on paper than speaking them. His troubles at the bank were not abating, he wrote, and he confessed to an increasingly dire certainty that the affair would end badly for him. He joked that his only consolation was that he might end up in Cañon City with the chance of an occasional glimpse of her or, at least, a daily sense of her proximity.

He told her that he had been taking long rides at his family's ranch, and that they were his only source of peacefulness and hope. He described the fall colors on the mesas and the changes in the air and in the light wrought by the new season. He confided that the only things that kept him from simply riding on and away forever were the sorrow and shame that he knew it would cause his family. He was filled with anger, he wrote, about the betrayal that he felt ever more certain the bank president was plotting against him, and at his own inexcusable stupidity for providing him the opportunity.

> *There is a small cabin that sits on a knoll in an aspen copse. My grandfather built it when he first cleared this land for cattle. Later, he built a big house at the other end of his property that still serves as my father's home. But the cabin was where my grandfather spent his first years, and it is filled with his presence, still. The logs were cut by his saw and axe, stripped by his adze, and chinked by his hand. Inside, there is nothing left but an old broken chair. The windows have no glass or curtains and the wind dances through as freely as swallows skimming a pond. There is a stream nearby, and I have taken to sitting in the*

old chair in the quiet of evening, listening to the music of the water and seeing its colorful tumble imitated by the play of sunset in the aspen leaves.

Although only briefly, and never fully, I am able to escape my current dilemma when I sit in the cabin. I am touched by something there that is as constant and comfortable as the rest of my life is uncertain and harrowing. I do not know if it is the spirit of my grandfather, who was a faultless, honest man, or if it is God who is challenging me to reinstate the belief and faith of my childhood. Or, perhaps, it is the simple force of Nature that bows to no law or judgment of men. Whatever it is, I wish with all my heart that I could retain the pleasure of it, the sweet relief of it, for longer than the fleeting interludes when I sit alone, the day's light softening into night. I wish, too, that you could be there with me, feeling the free breezes, tasting the freshness of the air, hearing the stream sing.

Alas, my wishes seem worse than impossible. They are scorned and derided by the facts of who you and I are and what we have done. Like a thunderhead taking over the sky, the light of my wishes is crowded out, completely obscured by the fear and dread of what I know is and will be.

Anise had read and re-read the letter countless times in the few days since its arrival. The scene that Hillman described was as vivid to her as if she herself was seated in the broken chair, the wind on her face, the stream's song in her ears. She shared with her new friend the fugitive solace of the place that he described so lovingly. And, like him, she shared the desolation of being unable to hold on to it. Nothing she had ever read joined a smile so closely to a tear.

That night in bed, dreaming, she felt him come to her. She felt his lips on hers, his naked chest pressed to hers, his force between her thighs. She cried out, releasing herself to his urgent need, and he was gone. She woke up. The night was dark and moonless, the quiet impregnable. For a moment she didn't know where she was, whether she was awake or still in a dream. Her nightdress was hiked high above her knees and damp with sweat.

"Mr. Hillman?" she said aloud. "Walter?"

The sound of her own voice broke the spell of the quiet and she knew then where she was. The dream had been so vivid, so real, that she could scarcely credit that it had not actually happened, that Walter Hillman had not been with her, that the passion that she had felt, had given herself over to, had been no more than a nocturnal fantasy. She had never, in reality, felt his nakedness against hers, never known the feel or taste of his lips, and yet, as she lay in the blackness of her cell, she knew all of that, knew his feel and his taste, with ineluctable certainty. She was not accustomed to dreaming of men, of a man she scarcely knew, of making love with all inhibition abandoned. She smiled as she fell back to sleep, wondering if she would dare tell him about it in a letter, or in person if he came to visit.

❈ ❈ ❈

The light that had filtered like gold dust through the cabin window had lost both its color and its warmth as Walter Hillman sat and tried desperately to make the words he wrote express his feelings. He had walked to the cabin that afternoon instead of riding. He had quit the bank early on the pretext of a customer meeting. As he passed the president's office, a wave of nausea and repulsion welled up in him at the smug nod directed to him. He felt a murderous hatred for the man and something not unlike it for himself.

When he reached his grandfather's cabin, he found in it nothing of the solace that it had of late afforded him. He realized that the wash of events, the tide of what had been and was to be, had eaten away at his hope like the ocean's tide relentlessly eroding a child's abandoned sand castle.

He crumpled the paper he had been laboring to fill with words that had true meaning and threw it across the empty room. He wanted to believe that he had fallen in love, that in the midst of all that was so wrong in his life, there was one thing, at least, that was right and good. But he no longer had any trust in his feelings. He felt in his heart that he was as unprincipled in spirit as he was in his actions. There was no reason not to fall in love with Anise. She was beautiful and intelligent and kind. He questioned, though, the authenticity of his newfound feelings for her and his motivation for encouraging them in himself. He was drowning, and she was the lone buoy that he could clasp and hang to in the hope for his own survival. It was need he had, he remonstrated himself, not love. It was a need to have love, not to give love. How could he give love when his every waking moment, and even his sleep, was informed by hurt and rancor?

He shivered, but not because of the coolness taken on by the breeze. From a deep pocket inside his mackinaw, he pulled out a revolver that had been his grandfather's and that he had first learned to shoot as a child. Then, it had seemed enormously heavy to him, a cannon that required both hands and all his strength to hold steady. The first time that he had fired it, the kick of the recoil was enough to nearly dislocate his shoulders; if his grandfather hadn't been standing at his side, anticipating the effect of the gun's explosion, his strong, sure hand ready to arrest the violent reaction of it, Walter's hands, so tightly clasped around the butt of the gun, would have leapt up and smashed into his face.

"A gun like this is not a toy," his grandfather told him, "it's a tool and these days not one you should ever have need to use. It's no good for hunting, and the law's no longer a thing to be taken in your own hands. Still, it's something that can't hurt to know how to use, so long as you know who you are and are happy in that knowledge. A gun can make a weak man suddenly strong, and that's a bad thing. It can also make a strong man weak, and that's perhaps worse."

Walter didn't understand his grandfather's words — not the ones about a strong man, at least.

"A strong man," his grandfather explained, "is willing to stand on his own, if he has to, against what he believes to be wrong. He's even willing to die for it. But I don't believe he should kill for it. Taking another man's life has never rid the world of wrong. If a man turns a gun on another man to exert his will, he has given up his strength. If he can't put the gun down and walk away, he may as well turn it on himself."

The words had impressed Hillman, but in a general way, as part and parcel of his grandfather's code of right and wrong, of his philosophy of life, and not so much as individual or specific words. Like so many others that his grandfather had freely shared with him, the words had circulated in his memory as indistinct but integral pieces of an overall body of wisdom. Now they formed in his mind with acute and detached clarity. And he knew that he was the man his grandfather had so long ago alluded to: a strong man grown weak; a man who had determined to take another man's life in an attempt to right a wrong.

He shivered again and held as tightly to the gun butt as he had the first time as a child.

CHAPTER ELEVEN

The first time Waggoner read of himself in a newspaper, he was in a café in Salt Lake City. It was a small place serving large plates of steak and eggs, pancakes, sausages, fried potatoes, and good coffee. It was bustling with morning business, the waitresses scribbling orders and calling them to the cook like clues to a guessing game.

"Sunup double on a doggie."

"Three flaps."

"Humpty Dumpty off the wall, a pair of porkies, home on the range."

"Humpty easy-up, double doggie, side-flaps."

"Cup of mud."

The vernacular of the place was familiar to the other customers, and they used it in ordering. Waggoner, baffled, resorted to standard English and ordered a poached egg on toast, three sausages, and home-fried potatoes.

"Humpty in a steam bath, on a shingle, porkies on a date with a chaperone, home on the range," called the waitress.

Waggoner enjoyed the quotidian normalcy of the café. It felt like a haven, a place where no one had anything more pressing on their mind than what to order for breakfast. The hum of conversation, the clatter of dishes, the waitresses' smiles, despite the burden of trays crowded with heaped platters, and the splashes of gravy and syrup already mottling their fresh uniforms, conspired to make the place seem sealed off from life's greater concerns, from whatever worries or pressing urgencies the diners had come from or were bound for. For the time being, inside the bright, crowded eatery, everyone was taking pleasure in this interlude of insouciance. Waggoner sat quietly waiting for his food, enjoying his anonymity and the café's satisfying sounds and smells.

A man slid into the seat opposite and nodded. He asked the waitress for two Humpties, off the wall, double doggie, side-flaps, and a cup of joe. Then he opened the paper he had with him and began to read. The waitress brought Waggoner his breakfast and he began to eat, the man across from him now clucking and chuckling at something in the news. When the waitress returned with his order, he put the paper down on the table, and Waggoner nearly choked on a bite of food as he saw his picture on the front page.

"You read about this bank job in New York?" asked the man as he took a mouthful of scrambled eggs and cut into his steak.

Waggoner shook his head, unable to speak.

"It's a doozie," said the other. "A fella from over in Colorado knocked off six banks at once for half a million. They're callin' it the crime of the century. And they have no idea where the guy is."

As he cut into his steak he looked expectantly at Waggoner, obviously wanting to share details of the story. Waggoner removed his glasses in the hope of becoming less recognizable and was glad of not wearing his fedora, as he had been when the photograph was taken.

"Half a million?" he asked, bowing his head to his plate and busying himself with his suddenly tasteless food. "Six banks at once? How'd he manage that?"

The other man snorted. "Don't know that I understand how he did it, exactly. Something to do with telegrams between banks and bank drafts and such. Turns out the bank robber's a banker. President of some podunk bank in some little town nobody's ever heard of."

"You don't say," commented Waggoner without lifting his eyes.

"Yessir. The fella must have brass balls, I'll say that. Walked right into one of those New York banks and lightened its load by five hundred thousand that shouldn't even have been there in the first place, I guess. It was all money sent in from other banks, 'cause the hick banker told 'em to." The man laughed. "Serves those New York bastards right, if you ask me. They think they own the damn world. If I had a chance to take their money, you wouldn't have to ask me twice."

The waitress came to refill the man's coffee.

"Hey, Sugar. D'you read about this?" He held up the paper and the waitress fumbled in her pocket for her reading glasses, then scanned the headline and Waggoner's portrait.

She whistled. "I could use some of that applesauce," she opined. "Wonder if he's married? Kinda plain, ain't he? Sorta meek in the mouth. Half a million, though. He wouldn't have to be Gary Cooper."

"He's a banker," said the man, as if that explained Waggoner's unprepossessing appearance.

The woman nodded. "Oh, yeah? Well he's got one up on my banker. That bloodsucker's on me like a tick if I go a day late on my loan." She looked as if she wanted to spit. "I wish I had the one in the picture. Doesn't seem like he'd much care if I never paid back a penny."

The woman laughed and the man joined her, and they began to chat amiably about the low esteem in which they held bankers generally, and theirs in particular. Waggoner had no appetite for his food but ate it as best he could, wishing to give neither of them reason to remember him.

"It's been a pleasure," he murmured as he finished and stood, looking at the floor.

The waitress handed him his check for the cashier. "You come back soon," she chirped paying him no more attention than she would have someone pouring catsup on the home-fried potatoes she served.

"Will do," Waggoner said and turned away, happy that his face was so forgettable. He made his way to the cashier and then to the door. On every other table or lap he saw himself staring from the front page of the Salt Lake paper. It felt as if he were in a nightmare, one that had started out as a sweet dream.

Out on the street, overwhelmed for a moment by the bright Utah sun, he stood uncertainly, not knowing quite what to do or which way to turn. He had originally considered going to Canada or Mexico, but he had decided against the one as too cold and the other as too hot. Europe, he had discounted as being stuffy and inhospitable. The rest of the world he considered too far away and too foreign to contemplate. He had finally resolved on San Francisco, and his plan, until a few moments earlier, had been to head there straight from Salt Lake. Bulkeley Wells was living in San Francisco. He imagined that his old friend would not object to taking him in for a while, harboring him until things blew over or resolved themselves. He thought his friend might welcome an old crony, especially if things for Wells were in the dumps. Now, that seemed a bad idea. If the story was already abroad, reaching Salt Lake, it would surely be known in San Francisco. As well as in every other big city. Regardless of his forgettable appearance and demeanor, cities posed a higher risk of recognition. Not everyone would be as blithely obtuse as the waitress and the man in the café. And it would only take one person — someone crossing the street with him, a taxi driver, a doorman, a different waitress, a different café customer — and he would be made out, and a call would be put through to the police.

He put his glasses back on. He would have preferred not to, but he had no choice. He was nearly blind without them.

He moved away from the front of the café, wanting to avoid the steady stream of people entering and emerging. He paused halfway down the block and turned away from the street, studying the pictures in a travel office window, feigning interest in the spas and resorts they advertised, trying to keep out of view and collect his thoughts.

"Tired? Bored? City Blues Have You Down?" one of the posted resort flyers inquired in large bold typeface. Waggoner read the smaller print beneath: "Come to the Cambria Resort for peace, privacy, and privilege. Do as you please or do nothing at all. Forget the world and remember your dreams."

Waggoner turned again and moved on. As he walked, his steps grew less and less uncertain. A resort could be just the place for him. He would be nothing more than another face among strangers there, just one more of an ever-changing roster of guests in a place where people were eager to mind no one's business but their own, and where the news was something they mostly cared not to know. The Cambria, its flyer had advised, was in New Market, Wyoming, near Cheyenne. Waggoner was only a few blocks from the Salt Lake bus station. He tucked his chin to his chest and quickened his step.

❀ ❀ ❀

The Cambria suited Waggoner nicely. It was not a lavish or even luxurious resort, but neither was it seedy. While it had horse riding, boating, nature outings, and such, its central attraction was clearly gambling. Indeed, since he had arrived, he had perceived no one taking advantage of any amenity other than gambling. He played a bit of faro himself, but then stuck mostly to poker. There were some accomplished players, and the stakes were rich enough to make things interesting. Luck, once so elusive, seemed to be with him. He was dealt good cards and drew well. He began to bet less carefully and his winnings multiplied. There was no particular delight, however, in his victories. Had he been home in Telluride at the Big Swing or the Pastime with Harry Miller and J.L. Segerberg, Joe Oberto, George Goldsworthy, and the others, he would have felt very merry taking their cash. Taking money from strangers, regardless of their talents, provided no great joy.

From the time that he had left New York, Waggoner had made no particular effort to cover his tracks. Even after his close brush in Salt Lake, he persisted in the belief that, as long as he did not invite attention, he could move along unnoticed. He had no new identity forged, no disguise, no bogus credentials. He had not considered that any of that would be necessary, but he had seriously underestimated the publicity and public reaction that would ensue from his act. He was happy to find, at the Cambria, that city papers were invariably stale by at least a few days. Still, they were available, and the news, although not fresh, eventually reached the resort. A clear geographical divide was evident in the reported versions of his act. He was heralded a hero from Detroit to Denver, while the eastern papers mostly excoriated him as a common thief and bamboozler.

Waggoner hadn't realized how contemptuous the general western population was toward Wall Street banks and brokerages. Times were stretched thin, not just in Telluride. People all over the western states seemed prone and even eager to blame their troubles on speculative greed emanating from New York. In the western papers that Waggoner read, the newspapermen made no attempt to disguise their delight in the New York banks' dilemma. Where the eastern reporters called him a "seedy hick" and a "red-necked shyster from the sticks," the western ones dubbed him a "modern Robin Hood" and described him as a "financial genius" and a "dazzling financier." He was particularly delighted with mention made of him in Will Rogers's popular syndicated column, which he cut out, folded, and put in his wallet.

> Seems a good old country boy banker got the best of the New York swells at their own game. Mr. C.D. Waggoner from Telluride, Colorado, pulled a fast one for five hundred grand that has left the city boys scratching their heads and upset in their paunches. Now, if a city banker had pulled just such a fast one on a country boy, you'd probably never hear a word about it, and he'd end up Secretary of the Treasury.

It had actually taken several days for the story to hit the press. As Waggoner had expected, the New York banks had been in no apparent hurry to have it publicized. It was a Denver reporter who first broke the news on September 6th, and Waggoner recognized as soon as he read it that the contents of his letter to McFerson had been divulged.

Waggoner assumed he would, somewhere, somehow, be caught, another reason that he eschewed disguise and an alias. He knew how the system worked once it started. It wouldn't take long, he knew, before the FBI, Pinkerton sleuths, and every flatfoot in the country was hoping to make a name for himself by his apprehension. What he didn't know was how long it would take and whom it would be who finally put the pinch on him.

There were practical matters to consider, as well. For one thing, he had purloined no extra cash for himself. He had extinguished significant debt, but what was being termed "the heist of the century" by the journalists had put nothing in his actual pockets. He had sent his wife a draft for five thousand dollars from New York and had written a note to her to cash it immediately. He wished now that he had kept it for himself, as he was certain she had not cashed it, and would not. She would not have known, at the time, that the money was stolen, but the alarm bells of her intuition, he imagined, must have been ringing loudly. He had also sent instructions to his sister's lawyer in Olathe to have several pieces of property deeded over to her and to Mary. This beneficence his wife, undoubtedly, would have greeted with further suspicion.

Waggoner wished he could have confessed to Mary. He rationalized that she was better protected by not knowing, but the fact was that his disclosure was impeded by more than that. His wife was a person who had never done anything wrong in her whole life, at least not deliberately. Waggoner had dared not imagine her mortification should he reveal to her the true nature of his trip to New York and the reason that they could not return immediately to Telluride. By now, of course, she knew. What she thought, he could not know exactly. Did she esteem him in any way a hero, like the western newspapers, or more of a scoundrel, like those from the East? Knowing how much she loved Telluride, he allowed himself to imagine that she would applaud his efforts to get funds to the town's depositors.

As more and more newspapers carrying his story and his picture arrived at the Cambria, Waggoner stopped visiting the gaming tables and chose odd hours to dine when less people would see him. He might have checked out early, but he had paid for a week, and he imagined that cutting short his stay would invite questions and curiosity that he preferred to avoid. His end might be inevitable, but the longer he was able to postpone it, the better he thought his chances might be to sort things out: to get all the money he had taken to the people he believed should rightfully have it.

It was his next to last night at the Cambria. He had not yet decided definitively where he would go from there, but he had a few thoughts in mind. He was emboldened by how little attention had been paid him all week and reasoned that, especially as the novelty of his story wore off, he would find himself able more and more to pass unnoticeably. There was no shortage of small, secluded spas and resorts to choose from. If his luck at cards held out, he could finance his stays at them indefinitely.

He went to the resort's dining room late, after all but a few guests had eaten and retired to their rooms or to the casino. He ordered trout, a choice that did not disappoint him. The fish was accompanied by boiled new potatoes that had been drizzled in melted butter with chopped parsley and by carrots boiled in milk and glazed with honey. It was quite excellent food, and after initially declining a glass of wine, he had changed his mind. He was trying to catch his waiter's attention when he noticed the man at the reception desk looking at him. He dropped his arm, deciding he ought not, after all, change his order. Even such a small thing might make him stand out.

🐝 🐝 🐝

Sheriff Charles D. Howell of Newcastle, Wyoming, thought he was the butt of a prank call. The sheriff was not known for his sense of humor, and his patience tonight was worn particularly thin by a faint throb in his left big toe that he knew to be the harbinger of a pending attack of gout. The affliction would hobble him, physically and emotionally, for days: long, painful, hateful days. He had his foot propped up on his desk in a futile attempt to delay the inevitable.

"Who is this!" he demanded.

The caller re-identified himself as the new manager of the Cambria Resort.

"And you're telling me that C.D. Waggoner is staying there?" Howell did not try to disguise his disbelief.

"Sitting here looking at a menu, just as though he didn't have a care in the world," answered the caller.

"What makes you think it's Waggoner?" growled Howell, wondering if amputation was a feasible antidote to gout.

"That's how he registered: C.D. Waggoner from Telluride, Colorado." The manager spoke in a hushed tone, almost a whisper, that Howell considered overly theatrical. There was no one in the nation, just at that moment, who was being more assiduously pursued than C.D. Waggoner. Every police station and sheriff's office across America had been alerted. A picture of the fugitive banker had been widely circulated, and Howell had a copy on his office wall.

"What's he look like?"

The manager hesitated a moment, as if he were stealing a fresh peak at the subject to confirm his impression. "He's short, bald, big ears, glasses, little moustache. Kind of a round head."

Howell straightened up in his chair and felt his pulse quicken, which served to further accentuate the throb in his toe. "Okay," he said, suddenly adopting the same stage whisper as the manager. "I'm coming up there. Give me twenty minutes, and don't let him out of your sight." He paused, still not entirely convinced of his caller's integrity. The Cambria was a well-known gambling resort. It occurred to him that a couple of sharps might be laying odds right now on his gullibility. "Listen," he threatened, "if this is a goose chase, I'll have a warrant for your arrest quicker'n you can blow a fart. You read me?"

The manager breathed out as if he now wished he had never bothered to make the call. Howell allowed himself a moment of smug satisfaction for foiling the prank. But then he heard the manager say that he understood completely, and that he would keep Waggoner under tabs until the sheriff arrived.

Howell hung up his telephone and then quickly picked it up again and dialed. He put calls in to the county attorney, Preston McAvoy, and to his special deputy, Robert Spargeon. His words to both were the same: "Be ready in five minutes. I'll pick you up." To Spargeon he added, "Bring a gun."

Sheriff Howell recognized Waggoner immediately. Still, he was surprised by the banker's modest bearing. He had expected the fugitive to have at least some air of danger or daring about him, but, as he made his way toward the table where Waggoner sat alone, he detected nothing of either. If asked, he would have guessed that Waggoner was a college professor or an ornithologist. He would certainly never have made him out as a bank robber.

"Charles Delos Waggoner?"

Waggoner looked up from his dinner as if he had not noticed the grim-faced men as they had moved purposefully toward him. The leader of the group, the man who had spoken, was large and sturdily built. His nose, or his mouth, possibly both, seemed slightly off-center, and his jaw was like a bucket hanging from the end of a squared face that was rutted with creases, like permanent lines of suffering. The man looked to be in pain.

"Yes, I'm Waggoner." He rose calmly and with an affable smile. "Won't you join me for something to eat?"

The sheriff was caught off guard. "Well, sir," he said at last, "I'm afraid we won't be doing that, no sir."

"Do you mind if I finish my meal?"

Sheriff Howell was disarmed anew. He was also a little disappointed. He had imagined his quarry to prove not so easily brought in, not so pliant, and certainly not so ridiculously polite. Truth be told, he was starving and would have liked nothing better than to sit down and make short work of a fat steak. And then charge it to the county who could, in turn, pass it on to the Feds.

"Afraid that would be a no, too," he answered. "No dessert tonight. I'm putting you under arrest by order of the U.S. Federal Attorney in New York. You have the right to remain silent."

As Howell read him his rights, Waggoner helped himself to further bites of fish and carrots. When Howell had finished, he stood up from the table. The sheriff fumbled to free his handcuffs from his belt. Waggoner waved him off.

"That won't be necessary," he said softly.

Howell continued to disengage the cuffs. "Not a choice," he said.

"I see," answered Waggoner, and he held out his hands. The cuffs of his jacket, Howell saw, were frayed, his wrists thin and small-boned. As he locked the cuffs, he couldn't help but notice the incongruity of their hard, strong manufacture and the banker's small, slight hands. He took Waggoner by one arm and Spargeon took the other. As they exited the room, the few other diners and the staff stared. Howell glanced at his prisoner and saw that he was blushing with embarrassment. Passing by the man at the reception desk, Waggoner said, "I haven't paid for my meal."

Howell stopped, yet again stunned by Waggoner's manner.

"That's alright, Mr. Waggoner," spoke the manager. "Just sign here." He handed Waggoner a blank piece of paper with the resort's logo as a heading. Waggoner looked at him, puzzled. "It's not a bill," said the manager. "I'd like to have your autograph."

Sheriff Howell could all but refrain from pinching himself. He had one of the most wanted men in America under arrest, a man who had stolen in a single swipe more money than Howell would make in his lifetime, and he was wearing a tattered old jacket and worried about paying a three-dollar dinner bill. And, best of all, the man who had stoolied him was now asking for his autograph!

It was a rich feast of absurdity. As Waggoner signed the paper, Howell realized that from the moment the banker had stood to invite them to eat, he had been free from the hateful pain in his toe. With that realization, the pain returned. He grimaced and pulled Waggoner toward the door, favoring his good foot heavily as he walked.

CHAPTER TWELVE

Harry Miller sat alone in his barbershop and stared absently out the window. In times past, he would have been at his busiest on a Saturday morning, his shop crowded with men looking to get a trim and a shave and to catch up on each other's news. Harry always kept a bottle of whiskey in the shop, and the miners were never shy to take a capful or two. For some, it was the start of the day's revelry that would likely end with them trudging penniless home from Popcorn Alley or lying like a bag of beans, snoring and grinding their teeth, on a hard, narrow cot at the jail. For others, it was a small last hurrah before returning to the mines after a night of riotous diversion. Since Prohibition, Harry kept the whiskey disguised in a cologne bottle.

In the empty chair beside him the week's edition of the *Journal* lay folded as if unread. With an effort of will, the barber picked up the paper and read, again, the banner headline: "Waggoner Captured Tuesday Night Near Newcastle, Wyoming."

Beneath the headline, in bold but smaller print, beside a photograph of Waggoner in his customary fedora and bow tie, the lead line read: "Alone Responsible for Crime, he says, in Frank Statement." An accompanying piece in the column beneath the photograph announced, "Liens Filed This Week on Bank Shares."

None of what Harry read in the headlines was news to him. He was a shareholder of the Bank of Telluride and had already been informed by the banking commissioner's office that his shares would be held as security, pending investigation of the bank's affairs. A young man who had introduced himself as Lundgren had come into the shop two days earlier. With his neatly arranged hair, smooth face, and shiny shoes, Harry had known immediately that he was not looking at a customer coming through the door.

Lundgren had wasted no time with pleasantries, but explained to Harry that, under state banking law, each shareholder was responsible for twice the amount of their holding in the bank to settle any loss.

Harry had nodded that he knew that. In fact, if he had ever been informed of the extent of his potential liability, he did not remember.

The next day he was visited by another young man by the name of Emanuel Kleid from the office of the U.S. attorney; he would be part of the team prosecuting the Waggoner case. It had been Kleid who told him that Waggoner had been captured, that a warrant was being dispatched from New York to Wyoming to have him arrested and brought East for trial. Then he had told him to expect a subpoena to appear at Waggoner's trial as a witness.

Kleid was neither as neatly shorn nor as closely shaven as Lundgren had been, but Harry had resisted his natural inclination to offer his services.

"It's not that we suspect you of complicity," Kleid offered. He had a dry, clipped way of speaking that Harry imagined might be effective in court but unbearable at a card table. "We're just interested to know if Waggoner may have ever confided things that could have a bearing on the case. You understand."

Harry had nodded. As a rule, he disliked lawyers and considered Kleid no exception.

He would not be the only one in Telluride subpoenaed. Half the town, it seemed, was to be served.

"We'll pay your train fare, hotel, and meals, and give you a per diem for expenses," said Kleid, as if reciting facts to a jury. "Ever been to New York?"

"No," Harry shook his head. "Never had the notion."

"You'll like it," said Kleid.

"I doubt it," replied the barber.

Kleid made a mental note to alert his boss, John Tuttle, U.S. District Attorney for New York, that Miller could prove to be reticent on the stand. He would recommend that Tuttle be as tough as possible in his questioning.

When Kleid left, Harry held the door for him but pretended not to see the hand that was proffered. He turned back into his shop, leaving the attorney posed stupidly with his hand extended. Kleid turned to the street and smiled to think of how Tuttle would make hick salad of the surly barber.

Harry had again put the newspaper down, but he returned to it and read. He was not surprised to learn that his friend had registered under his own name. That was textbook Buck, he thought, bluffing to the end. He smiled, too, to read that Waggoner had invited the three men who caught him to sit down and have dinner. The rest of the articles, though, gave him no similar amusement. The quotes attributed to his friend were disoriented and contrived. Buck Waggoner was possibly the quietest and most modest man that Harry had ever known. To get three consecutive sentences out of him in a conversation was a feat. Harry had sat through many evenings playing cards with the banker when he had literally said no more through the hours than pass, raise, call, and fold. Now, in the paper, he was quoted going on and on in an almost arrogant way about how he had planned and executed the heist with no help, how he had done it for the sole purpose of saving his depositors from loss, that he had paid no consideration to the interests of the shareholders, who, he said, "...understood when they acquired their interest that it entailed the risk of loss."

In addition to trimming Waggoner's hair every few weeks, and sitting regularly with him at the same gambling table, Harry had met formally with Waggoner and the other shareholders every quarter to be updated on the bank's condition. Like him, the other shareholders, of whom there were only a dozen, were men and women who had lived in Telluride for many years. They had known Buck Waggoner for at least two decades, some of them, like Harry, even longer. Most of them had business connections with the banker through his bank and outside it. There was not a good reason that Harry could think of for Buck Waggoner to suddenly turn his back on his shareholders. It was entirely out of character. Unless, he thought, one of two things, maybe both, were true: Waggoner had lost his mind, or his hands were dirty.

"Give me ten months and I will turn the Bank of Telluride completely around from its current circumstances," Waggoner was quoted in the paper.

Harry frowned. This was simply not the way Buck spoke: He was neither assertive nor bold. And, to the day that he left for New York, he had never indicated to the shareholders that the bank's "circumstances" were anything to seriously worry about. What also troubled Harry, setting the brow above his dark eyes in a furrow as he read, was the contradiction between Buck's claims about protecting his depositors and the way he described how he disposed of the stolen funds. Notes of the Bank of Telluride owed to New York banks were paid off, and a note of his personally, and of his company, Norwood Land and Cattle, the same. Apart from collateral released to the Bank of Telluride upon repayment of its debt — bonds and securities, mostly — the only funds that had come close to getting to the depositors was fifty thousand in cash and securities held as collateral by the New York banks and released upon payment of the Bank of Telluride's debt. And those funds had been seized by McFerson, the bank commissioner. So, no depositor had, as yet, received a sou. As things appeared, none soon would.

Harry knew that Buck Waggoner was not a "financial genius," a "wizard," or a "dazzling financier," as the reporters were dubbing him. He was assuredly smart enough, though, to make certain half a million dollars, once pried from its New York guardians, would arrive where he intended it to go.

He sighed and shook his head. One thing was certain: He would never do or say anything against his friend. Whether Buck was as guilty as Judas and the shareholders lost their britches, it didn't matter. He had known Buck Waggoner always as a good, honest, and fair man. If President Hoover himself came in for a trim and a nip from the cologne bottle and asked Harry to rat his friend out, he wouldn't. The rest of the world be damned, he thought. Buck Waggoner was one of Telluride's own, one of its best. For Harry, that meant all comers were welcome. He would gladly take them on.

🐝 🐝 🐝

Alta Cassietto made the decision to go to New York quite quickly. She had not been asked or ordered to go as a witness, and it wasn't necessary for her to go as a reporter, for the story was already being covered by reporters from virtually every city in the country. C.D. Waggoner was her neighbor, his son a schoolmate, his wife a woman whom she saw almost every day. What had occurred had shaken her town to its core. She could not sit back and wait for the news to come by wire from New York. She needed to be there. She needed to see Buck Waggoner, hear his testimony with her ears, listen to the charges of the prosecution, and let no one else decide for her what was or was not the truth of the banker's motives. She conferred with Frank McNamara, and he concurred that the newspaper should share half the cost, at least, of her expenses. The problem was that along with everyone else's, the business's funds had been frozen at the bank by the commissioner. Frank and Alta traded names of people who might lend her the cash as they worked on the weekly edition of the paper. Alta was reading through wire releases and discarding them until one caused her to linger.

"We'll have to fit this in," she said.

"What is it?"

"Another sign of the times, I'm afraid. The Delta National Bank has had its doors closed. Fifty thousand dollars seems to have gone astray, and the vice president, Walter Hillman, has killed himself. He was found in a cabin on his family's ranch. Dear Lord, when will it all end?" She closed her eyes.

Frank whistled low and slow. "My God," he said. "I know the Hillmans. They've been ranching in Delta for near fifty years. I've met Walter. I would never have thought him to do a thing like that. Poor people." He clucked his tongue. "It's as if the damn world is falling apart around us."

Alta opened her eyes and waved off her colleague's lament. "If the world falls apart," she stated, "so be it. I just want to be sure to cover it. For now, I'm going to go see Dad Painter about New York. Be back in an hour."

She pulled her jacket from its hook. "If you don't want to stay any longer this evening," she told Frank as she went out the door, "that's okay. We can finish in the morning."

Frank nodded, but did not reply, his usual cheerfulness replaced by a dark fatalism.

For all her bravado, Alta's heart was also heavy. She had faith, though, just as the early miners had. Like them, she was a resolute optimist. She believed, ultimately, in a better future for Telluride and for the world. She had grown up hearing stories from her father of the suffering and tragedies that had so often beset her town. There were tales of avalanches, like those of 1902 that thundered two thousand feet down Greenback Mountain, coming in successive waves. The first turned three heavily constructed mine buildings, anchored with thick wire rope bolted into solid rock, into nothing but splinters. Tree trunks, three feet in diameter, were uprooted, and boulders, the size of cabins, were yanked from the ground and floated along in a snow mass seventy-five feet wide. The noise, her father had told her, "was like a hundred cannons all fired at once." The second slide came just as rescuers were stretched out in a line across the debris-strewn path of the first; twenty-four were killed. The survivors were frantically searching for the victims when yet a third release sent another slide crashing down the mountain. An hour later, a fourth and final avalanche, as ferocious as any of the first three, took more lives. In all, thirty-one people died that day. It was the second catastrophe within a year, as, during the previous summer, a fire had started in a stack of hay that was stored at the mouth of the Smuggler-Union Mine. The fire had quickly turned into a conflagration, and its heavy smoke was sucked into the mine, where a dozen miners, trapped, were blinded, choked, and killed by it.

At the time, there had been neither ventilation, nor emergency escape systems in place at the mine. The horror of the fire provided stimulus to the struggling unionist movement, and a period of violent altercations ensued with little good for the miners in the outcome. The state National Guard was ordered in to Telluride by the governor and put under the command of Bulkeley Wells, who had formed a small local militia that he called the Telluride Citizens' Alliance. The following November, the British manager of the Smuggler-Union, Arthur Collins, was assassinated, and the mine owners reinforced themselves with hired killers and vigilante tactics. Alta's father had emphatically insisted that Collins had been killed by non-union miners, with complicity from the mine owners, in order to discredit the unionists. Bulkeley Wells took over as manager of the Smuggler-Union and, shortly after he did, a bomb exploded under his bed while he slept, shattering all the windows in his house and hurling him into the night's cold darkness. As many miners had been, Alta's father was cynical of the purported unionist attack on Wells.

"Don' choo tink," she remembered him saying in his heavy Italian accent, "dat dey coulda ha' blowed dat prima donna to da moon iffa dey hadda wanted? Wha'? Dey dynamite trou harda rock all day an' dey on'y putta enougha powder under 'im to give 'im carpet ride?"

After the murderous snowslides that winter, Colorado State National Guard Adjutant General George F. Gardner proclaimed that the Telluride disasters were a "signal from the Maker" to miners for their "sins" against the owners. The unionists responded by killing a Smuggler-Union shift boss by the name of Barney. His body was dumped in heavy timber on the Coonskin Ridge. When it was discovered much later, the bones having been scattered by coyotes, his skull, still with remnants of red hair, was displayed in a window on Colorado Avenue.

Alta buttoned her jacket at the throat as she hurried up the Aspen Street hill. The summer had extended into a mild autumn, but its end was signaled by the chill of the nights. Ahead of her she could hear Cornet Creek as it splashed down its rocky course. On July 28, 1914, compliments of a vicious thunderstorm in the mountains near the creek's source and of late snowmelt, Cornet Creek had metamorphosed into a monstrous flood. The onslaught of the water and, along with it, boulders, trees, and great chunks of turf and forest floor was more than the narrow creek bed could contain. Worst of all, the sludge of mud and mine tailings turned the flood into an unnaturally magnified force. The creek overflowed and moved like accelerated lava into town, pushing houses off their foundations, filling them with its magma-like mud, or simply knocking them down. The ground floors of businesses on Colorado Avenue had to be evacuated. There had been only one human toll, but animals perished by the score, and the stench of death mixed with the microbial decay of the mud and sludge visited a pestilential air on Telluride for weeks.

The town had survived its fair share of mayhem, both natural and man-made, and as she stepped up to knock at Dad Painter's door, Alta held at bay any doubts about its ability to do so again.

Charles "Dad" Painter had been an early arrival in Telluride. He came in 1880, just a few years after the first claims were staked in Marshall Basin. He was the founder and, for better than forty years, the editor of the *Daily Journal*. He had also, for many years, owned the town's primary title abstract and insurance company. Now, well on in years, he was still mentally sharp and more than a little cantankerous. He had a special fondness for Alta, but spared her none of his gruffness.

"Seems a damn fool waste of money to me," he told her, stabbing at the smoldering logs in his fireplace with a long, old-fashioned poker. The logs flared to life, fiery sparks emitting that were sucked up past the flue. Alta noticed that the throw rug in front of the hearth was pocked and singed from sparks that had escaped the chimney's draft on other occasions.

Painter regarded the rekindled flames with satisfaction, then returned the poker to its hook. The room was small and comfortable, with two tall windows draped by dark velvet curtains. There were two leather armchairs, worn with age and shined by use, with lines, some of them creases, spreading like a road map across their seats and backs. Two of the room's walls were covered by built-in shelves, stained a rich hue of chestnut and crammed with books in no particular order. The majority of them had to do with mining and the rest with history. Without exception, they appeared to have been read and re-read more than once or twice. A small settee with a low table placed in front of it and a standing lamp beside it was against the third wall. On it, a large cat that, in its day, had been quite mighty, lay quietly oblivious, its heavy tail twitching from time to time as the feline napped.

The two leather chairs faced the fireplace, and when Painter was content that he had adequately revived the flames, he dropped down into one and looked across to the other where Alta sat. Painter's brow furrowed and his eyes squinted almost closed. Then he opened them and sighed through his nose. He would have liked to have a cup of tea, but he didn't fancy making it himself and didn't care to impose on his guest, however unexpected her visit. He thought of his wife and missed her, as he had every day and night since she had passed several years before.

"You know, of course," he grunted, "there'll be news folks there from all over the country. Hell, there'll be some there from around the damn world. I don't believe it's as if you're going to be able to top what they have to say. This is a big story, girl. All the papers will have their aces on it." He snorted. "Why, hell, we got scooped right here in our backyard. What makes you think it's important, and worthwhile financially, to have the *Journal* there?"

Alta had been prepared for this kind of interrogation. Dad Painter was notorious for his directness, and he liked putting people on the spot. If someone gave up his side of an argument too readily, Painter would, as often as not, adopt it for himself, just to keep the discussion lively.

"This is *our* story," answered Alta, calmly but firmly. "It doesn't matter if every paper from every civilized country in the world sends a reporter, or a dozen of them and photographers. None of them will be able to tell our story as we can. And they shouldn't be allowed to speak for us. We shouldn't let them. I don't try to cover the gang wars in Chicago or President Hoover's speeches. I leave those to reporters better placed and better informed. This isn't like that."

"No? Why not? There's nothing about this story that any correspondent worth his ink couldn't investigate, research, and turn into a Pulitzer Prize. And most of the hounds you'll come across are syndicated. They can sell their stories before they've even written their bylines. Hell, they probably already have their expenses covered and their publisher drooling over the profits."

This was not a large exaggeration, but Alta knew better than to concede an early point, however compelling. "It's not about fame and fortune," she declared. "Our paper will be no better known, no more prosperous, no closer in line for any prizes after this trial than before. But the name of Telluride will be on everyone's lips. Perhaps for a week, maybe a month...I don't know. What I do know, though, is that no one writing about our town, our history, our bank and its president will tell the story as it should be told. Why, you can see it already. Half the mob is making Buck Waggoner out as the shrewdest fraudster that ever lived, and Telluride as a hick town that's happy to turn a blind eye as long as there's money enough left for one more bet or to pay for a shady lady." Gambling and prostitution, although not nearly as prevalent as in Telluride's days of plenty, were still staples of the town's economy and Alta knew that Painter deplored both with equal passion. "The other half," she went on, "is making him out as a prince of thieves forced to turn to crime by the greed of others."

"If you ask me," countered Painter, "there *are* more hicks than fence posts around here these days and half of them spend more time at cards and hoochey-coo than they do at making a living. And as for your 'peasant prince,' I'd say he's writing his own tall tale. I read his quotes when they caught him in Wyoming. If I didn't know better, I'd have thought he was from Sherwood Forest, not Telluride."

Alta, of course, had read the quotes, as well. Waggoner had been unequivocal, representing himself as being forced to extravagant lengths to protect his bank and his town against the depredations of the big banks that were abandoning the town now that riches were not so easily made.

"He may be a Robin Hood," she said, "or he may be an arch crook. You know him as well as I do — better, in fact. What do you think?"

Painter shook his head. "Damned if I know what to think. I've known Buck Waggoner since the day he arrived here as a silly-looking pale kid who wouldn't have known how to steal Blind Schwab's shoe polish tins. If you had asked me before, I would have put him at the very end of the list of men who might do such a thing. I know one thing for sure, though: his uncle James must be rolling over in his grave. In the crash of '93, when the government stopped buying silver and it looked as if the town, and maybe the whole damn nation, might not survive, James Brown used his personal fortune to keep the bank afloat and his depositors whole. Hard to believe the same blood could run in both their veins.

"You know, Buck's got the gambling bug bad," Painter spat the words with contempt. Alta had never been to a gaming table of any kind, but she had heard it said, more or less directly, depending on the source, that the bank president was a habitué of more than one of Telluride's gambling venues. "Can't be good for the Robin Hood proponents, can it?" Painter said.

Alta smiled and shook her head. "No, not good," she allowed. "The point is, though, with so much uncertainty surrounding this whole case, with so many pieces strewn about, ready to be picked up and stacked one way or the other, for him or against him, I don't think it should be left to outsiders, people with no personal interest in the facts, to pick those pieces up and pile them as they choose, depending on their own self-interests."

The two went back and forth for over an hour. The point that finally swayed Painter to Alta's side had nothing to do with the case itself, with whether Buck Waggoner was saint or sinner, or whether his story, and Telluride's, was best told by a native. Instead, it was that Alta was willing to pay money of her own to realize her ambition. Painter had even less time for panhandlers and freeloaders than he did for gamblers and whores. He knew that Alta was supported solely by her own income and he knew, as well, that her income was not ample. That she was willing to sacrifice her own personal savings for something that she felt strongly about, which would garner her no particular benefit, was all that he really needed to know. In fact, he had known it within minutes of her arrival, for she had specified that she sought only half of the funds required. Still, he had wanted her to fully argue her case. He would not have wanted her to think he was growing soft. And he relished the company. Books and memories were too often now his only companions.

Alta was still talking, still positing her opinions, when Painter held up his hands in surrender. "You win," he said simply, then slowly rose from his chair and went to a wall panel, which he opened. Inside was a squat, steel safe. After deftly twirling the lock, he pulled open its door and removed a bundle of cash. Alta was not surprised to see many more like it arranged neatly in the safe.

"How much do you need?"

"The train, to and from, will cost seventy-five dollars. I estimate the hotel..."

"Take five," said Painter and handed her five notes of one hundred dollars, each.

"But, Dad," she cried, "that's far too much!"

He held up his hands again. "If you have some left over, put it under your mattress. But don't scrimp in New York. We don't want people thinking we're poor hicks."

Alta took his hands and kissed him on the cheek.

"Do us proud," he whispered. "Get the real story."

CHAPTER THIRTEEN

Elwood Rabenold was the Bank of Telluride's Denver attorney. Samuel Crump, a criminal lawyer, would represent Waggoner in New York. As Rabenold knew Waggoner and the affairs of his bank, Crump had requested him to serve as co-counsel for the defense. He had also asked him to interview Waggoner at the Denver train station when the banker's train arrived from Wyoming on its way to Chicago.

Rabenold had not consciously chosen banking law; he had drifted into it as a young attorney and found that it suited him. He was conservative by nature and lacked the imagination and verve that many other areas of the law seemed to require. Banking law, generally, was as dry as toast and as easily digestible, and that was fine with him. There were more lucrative fields of practice, but he was not dismayed by middling financial success. He had received a modest inheritance from his father and had safely invested it in low-risk government bonds.

He could have passed for a banker. He always dressed in staid suits, his white shirt collar stiffly pressed, his shoes plain but polished. He wore a fob watch in the pocket of his waistcoat and he pulled it out with an unconscious flourish. The train was late, something Rabenold prided himself on never being.

He turned away from the track and busied himself with choosing a newspaper from a kiosk that had a large selection from around the country. A photograph of Waggoner, in the custody of a sheriff, whose large, square face seemed creased as if he were in pain, was on the front page of many of them. Rabenold knew that he was not a creative person, but even if he had been blessed, or cursed, with an artist's sensibility, he could never have contrived to picture Waggoner as either hero or villain. Depending on which paper he had read over the past days, that was how the small, funny looking, banker was portrayed. The idea of Waggoner being a fugitive bank robber, one of the most wanted men in America, was at the very edge of plausibility.

Rabenold had known Buck Waggoner for better than ten years. He had visited him in Telluride, had dined in his home on several occasions, and, in turn, had hosted him as often in Denver. Had he been asked to name a man who was his personal equal in ordinariness and lack of panache, he might well have named Waggoner. The banker was mild, shy, softly spoken, and, so Rabenold had always believed, as straight as an arrow.

Rabenold was thankful that his client's itinerary had not been made public. He generally deplored newsmen because of their dedicated inattention to facts and their penchant to misquote. In his opinion, journalists, especially in groups, shared many of the least desirable characteristics of a traveling sideshow.

At 8:30 PM, fully thirty-five minutes behind schedule, the Wyoming train pulled into the station with the squeal of steel braking against steel, steam and smoke spewing from it like volumes of frozen breath. A flurry of commotion ensued with porters racing their dollies to be of first service and conductors calling out and jumping to the platform from the still-moving train. Passengers inside the train cars stood, stretched, reached for their baggage, or pressed their faces to the windows, while new passengers gathered in disorderly queues to climb aboard.

Rabenold did not see Waggoner descend from the train, but at the end of the throng that had disgorged onto the platform he saw him, straddled by two federal agents, his hands locked in cuffs that he tried, with modest success, to keep hidden by holding his hat. The agents accompanying him were large and solid looking. Waggoner's diminutive form was exaggeratedly dwarfed between them. Rabenold stepped toward the three and raised his hand. Waggoner saw him and spoke to his guards, who let him advance to greet the lawyer.

"Hello," said the banker, smiling brightly, as if they were meeting to have dinner or go to a show. "Good of you to come see me. I'm afraid we haven't much time. The train leaves again in quarter of an hour. Shall we have a lemonade?"

It occurred to Rabenold, suddenly and clearly, that Crump's inclination to an insanity plea might not be at all off the mark. He had expected to find Waggoner haggard and worn, listless. He was not prepared for this air of lightheartedness.

"I'm afraid there's no lemonade available, that I'm aware of," he answered, making a show of looking around the station, although he knew it intimately, knew that there had never been a lemonade stand or anywhere selling it, even in the hot summer months.

"Oh, well," replied Waggoner, good-naturedly. "I didn't actually suppose there would be. It's just that I'm a bit parched. A lemonade seemed just the ticket."

Rabenold took his client by the arm and felt him tighten, perhaps by the pressure on his wrists caused by the handcuffs. He noticed, too, that Waggoner's fingers pressed more firmly on his fedora, so he eased his grip on the small man's arm.

"We'll get a drink of water from the fountain, if that's alright."

"Splendid," said Waggoner, letting Elwood lead the way. "You know," he said genially as they walked, the two agents trailing at a discreet distance, "if I could just have a little time, no more than a few months, I could have the bank in perfect order. No one need lose a penny."

Rabenold was at a loss to respond. His notion of Waggoner's sanity was firming. "Will you cooperate with the authorities?" he asked, thinking of no better response.

"How so?" asked the banker.

They had reached the water fountain and Rabenold turned the handle, avoiding embarrassment for Waggoner, who continued to keep his bound hands hidden by his hat.

"Thank you," said Waggoner. He bent and drank slowly. Rabenold was happy for the interlude.

"Well," he said when Waggoner had finished and straightened. "It seems you have tied a rather intricate knot by the various payments and transfers that you effected. Properly undoing it all might require your assistance."

Waggoner looked at him as if he were uncomprehending. "Any loss suffered by the New York banks," he replied in a tone of unflappable certainty, "or the Denver banks, for that matter, and any inconvenience or expense caused them, would give me nothing but the purest pleasure. What I did was solely in the interests of my depositors. If I were Mr. McFerson, I would arrange to distribute all the funds that I had credited to the bank without hesitation. Let the big banks squabble and cry foul all they please. No sir, I have no intention of cooperating in any form or fashion."

"You know that you will likely go to prison."

Again the banker looked at the lawyer blankly. "I do," he said. "Indeed, I have considered that I will not even make use of a defense attorney. I have no case to manipulate with clever ploys or facile words. I stole from the rich to give to the poor. I'm unashamed of it and ready to face the consequences. Frankly, I'm relieved it's over. I was tiring quickly of life on the run, always expecting a hand to clasp me from behind, never knowing when the door might be kicked in and I would be dragged from bed like some common wretch.

"Do you happen to have ever heard of Bob Meldrum?" he asked, changing the subject abruptly without a pause.

Rabenold hesitated, astounded anew by Waggoner's unexpected manner. "Can't say I have, no."

""Well," said Waggoner, "after Arthur Collins was killed, he was manager of the Smuggler-Union. You know the mine, of course?"

Rabenold nodded.

"Yes," said Waggoner, as if distracted from his own line of thought. "The Sheridan vein, the largest in the region. It was six feet wide and was worked for a length of four miles and a depth of three thousand feet. The gold assayed at one thousand, two hundred dollars a ton. Imagine the quality of it." He clucked and shook his head. "You know the claim was originally staked by two partners, Fallon and White. Unfortunately for Mr. White, he failed to pay one hundred dollars to have his portion properly surveyed and titled. Along comes a chap by the name of Ingram. He had apparently been poking about up in Marshall Basin, and prompted by some instinct, I suppose, he decided to measure White's extension of Fallon's claim. Sure enough, he discovered that it exceeded the legal limit of one thousand, five hundred lineal feet. So, without ado, he placed a stake on the excess. Called it the 'Smuggler'. Obviously not a man without a sense of irony. Well, sir, White's claim yielded nothing. Both Fallon and Ingram, on the contrary, struck it rich. In 1899, just fifty-one percent of the combined Smuggler-Union sold for fifteen million dollars to an eastern syndicate."

He paused. Rabenold had relinquished any hope of trying to speak to him sensibly about legal defenses and tactics. "And Bob Meldrum?" Rabenold asked.

"Ah, quite. Meldrum. After Collins was killed, I guess that would have been '02, and the unionists were intensifying their efforts, a number of the mine owners imported professional gunmen who were made deputy sheriffs. They were hard men, lightening on the draw and with a penchant for trouble. Of them all, Meldrum was the most dangerous. He was a killer, plain and simple. The first night that he arrived in town, he went to a union saloon that was filled with union men and sympathizers. He elbowed his way to the bar and pushed in between the two biggest, toughest characters in the place. He slammed his gun down on the bar. 'I'm Bob Meldrum,' he announced. 'You can always find me when you want me. Now, if any son of a bitch has anything to say, spit it out. Otherwise, I'm going to take a drink. Alone.' I believe he may have been English-born. Unlike the rest of his ilk, he was clever and articulate and could tell tales of his murders and exploits that would have made a novelist proud." Waggoner paused again for several moments. "You know," he continued quietly. "I often thought of Meldrum while I was on the run. I wished I could be more like him — not afraid of anything or anyone."

At these words, a whistle blew loud and shrill.

"All aboard!" shouted the conductor. "All aboard for Chicago!"

The two agents stepped between Rabenold and his client, and — as if he had merely dreamed the past fifteen minutes, merely imagined Waggoner's strange, disjointed words — the lawyer stood again on his own.

❋ ❋ ❋

The train to Chicago sped through the night. No longer did it toil carefully through canyon steeps or disappear into tunnels, where the geology of the mountains seemed with deliberate intent to impede passage by any but the highest soaring birds and sure-footed animals. There were no rock slides now to fear, no threats of mountain streams turned to deluge by unseen outbursts in high hidden basins. The awesome wrinkles and folds of the earth's crust were every moment left farther behind, the land now merely undulant between vast expanses of flatness. The train pushed through the absolute darkness with an unrelenting rhythm as if it would never, could never, slow down or stop.

Waggoner lay in his berth drifting in and out of restless sleep. Each time he woke he was surprised anew by the staccato cadence of the train and by the stertorous snoring of his two guardians. A dozen times since the agents had locked the door of the compartment and said goodnight, Waggoner had awoken disoriented, trying to remember where he was and why. He made no effort to consult his watch and would have been thwarted, anyway, in the attempt, by the compartment's impenetrable blackness. His suspicion, however, was that his bouts of wakefulness lasted longer than the interims of sleep and that the night still stretched far ahead.

It was difficult for him not to contrast his current circumstances with those of his original train ride, traveling the same track, but in the opposite direction, thirty-three years prior. Then, too, he had passed a fitful night, though the anxiousness that informed him had been of a different quality. He had been so young then, not just in years, but in understanding and experience. The boundaries of his world and the scope of his interactions with others had been so tightly circumscribed. There was an irony that he now recognized, but could not have at twenty-one, that his horizons after growing up on the plains of Illinois should become so enlarged, so stretched by life in Telluride, a town that was as hidden and hemmed in as the low lands of his home were open.

At night in his childhood hometown, the main street was inconsistently lit by gas lamps that flickered and often went out. At their best, they produced soft pools of light that occasional passersby strolled in and out of, like passing clouds illuminated by the moon. What a difference he had experienced on arriving in Telluride at night. It had been spring and the dark had not been the ink black curtain that he stared at now, unseeing. The darkness of the Telluride night had been almost tender, infused with remnants of light from a day that had been as clear and bright as any Waggoner had ever known.

As the Rio Grande Southern train approached Telluride, it was electric light that Waggoner could make out shining with uniform brightness from the street lamps of Colorado Avenue and from the town's houses, not light from burning kerosene. No other small town in the world, and not many cities, could boast of such illumination. To Waggoner, accustomed to reading by candlelight and to nocturnal shadows that spread like dark water from pockets of unsteady gaslight, the sight was as unexpected as it was unforgettable.

He later came to know the man responsible for Telluride's distinction, the man who could claim more than partial honor for the town's sobriquet, "Paris of the West." Lucien L. Nunn was not small enough to be considered a dwarf, but even in comparison to Waggoner, he was of insignificant stature. Only his head seemed to be of normal proportion, and in combination with his small body, it conspired to make him seem less than fully grown. Napoleon Bonaparte was his hero. As a young and no doubt precocious boy, he had prevailed on his parents to name his newborn brother after the famous French general and the sibling had, in fact, been called Bonaparte.

Whatever Nunn lacked in physical size, however, was made up for generously by shrewdness, acumen, and an unshakeable work ethic. He had arrived in Telluride in the mid '80s from Denver by way of Leadville and Durango, where he had operated small restaurants that had allowed him to survive, but barely. The problem may have been that the food he served had little to recommend it. Or it may have been that Nunn, for all his outward bluffness, could not bring himself to charge the poor miners that took their meals with him enough to earn him a decent return. Whatever the case, Nunn drifted to Telluride in its early days. He hired out as a carpenter initially, and then, seeing that the town was expanding with every new claim, managed to borrow money enough to buy vacant lots on Telluride's main street, on which he constructed buildings that he leased out at high rates. He was soon the largest property owner in town.

Although deeply grateful for the loan that the San Miguel Valley Bank had made him, he was alarmed by its underwriting standards. Any bank that would lend him money, he reasoned, must not be a very good bank. Looking into the matter, he discovered that the two men who had founded the bank had suffered a rift in their partnership, and that it was causing them to neglect their enterprise. Giving the bankers the few thousand dollars that he had managed to save since arriving in town and a note secured by a first deed of trust against all his commercial properties, Nunn took over ownership of the bank. His timing was impeccable. The Telluride mines were beginning to produce truly estimable quantities of high-yielding ore, and their owners were dedicated to expanding their operations. New claims were being staked daily. Whether new or existing, all the mines required capital, as did the entrepreneurs who rode the miners' tide like so much flotsam. Grocers, liverymen, haberdashers, saloon keepers, dance hall doyens — they all needed loans, short-term and long-term, to support their businesses. Money flowed like water, and its motion was largely circular: It came from the bank, and it returned to it.

In 1889, less than two years after acquiring the bank, Nunn suffered a setback. While not devastating in its financial consequences, it was bitter enough to sour him on banking and stimulated him to turn his tireless energies to other pursuits.

This was a story that Waggoner had heard recounted over and over. Each time it was embroidered with different details, embellished with additional facts and fictions. It was a story that had never ceased to entertain him, and one that had all the elements of the dime store novels about the Wild West that he had soaked up thirstily as a boy. Lying in his berth, the unexciting flatlands of the Midwest flying past invisibly, hidden by the deep cover of the moonless night, he thought of the story as it had first been told to him. He couldn't remember who the original storyteller was: It could have been Christmas Tree John, Old Dick Liner, the Moonshiner, or any number of other old-time raconteurs — it didn't matter which. The story itself he remembered in every detail.

Robert Leroy Parker was a young mule skinner working in Telluride. In later years, his mother would describe him as "a kind, good boy that went bad." Someone who helped steer him wrong was a horse rustler by the name of Mike Cassidy. Cassidy served as a father figure for Parker, whose own father he never knew, and the boy, when he was old enough to strike out on his own, adopted the rustler's last name. For a first name, he stuck with the nickname Butch. Parker, or Cassidy, had been working in Telluride for several months and had made no particular impression, good or bad. He worked, drank whiskey at the saloons, partook of an occasional dalliance with the red-light ladies, and liked to go on Sundays to the horse races outside of town, where he wagered modestly and sometimes rode as a jockey. The description of his daily life would have fit more than half the men in Telluride. Until, that is, one early summer day in June 1889.

On that day, Butch Cassidy rode into town dressed as if he were headed to his own wedding. He was freshly shaven and had on a suit and tie and a brand new derby hat. People who knew him as a mule skinner — a dirty, beaten-up cowboy hat pulled low over his eyes — would not have recognized him.

Butch pulled his horse up in front of the San Miguel Valley Bank, tied it to the hitching post, and went inside. The bank was not busy, and Cassidy waited for the few customers before him to settle their business. He held the door open for the last of them and, when they had gone out, he closed and locked it. Then he turned to the two tellers behind their protective grills and pointed a Colt six-shooter at each of them. When he walked back out the door, the bank had experienced its first robbery and was suddenly shy twenty-four thousand dollars. It was Cassidy's first bank job.

Mounting his horse, he fired several shots into the air, not an unusual pastime in Telluride in those days. He galloped out of town, a dust cloud trailing in his wake, like a challenge written on the wind.

L.L. Nunn was upstairs in his office at the time. He paid scant attention to the gunshots, assuming it was part of some drunken cowboy or miner revelry. When one of the tellers rushed into his office, flushed and frantic, Nunn leapt up and rushed downstairs and into the street. Nothing more than a thin trace of dust hung in the air where Cassidy had, minutes before, made his getaway.

Nunn commanded the tellers to summon the marshal. He was piqued — his face red, his lips thin and white. "I'm going after him," he cried. Unwilling to wait for the company of a posse, he rushed back inside to retrieve his pearl-handled revolvers and then rushed outside and climbed onto his horse. Charging out of town, he could see Cassidy's dust trail ahead of him, a half-mile or so. Nunn's horse was a good one, his best. He rode high up on its neck like a monkey in the circus. It may have been that he could have, eventually, caught up with Butch. The mule skinner-turned-robber, however, had not been fool enough to tackle the job on his own. Just before Society Turn, three miles west of town, two riders fell in beside Nunn from the trees where they had been hiding. They were Tom McCarty and Matt Warner, though Nunn could not have known that as both were masked. Their guns were leveled at the small banker.

Nunn returned toward town on foot, his holster emptied of the pearl-handled pistols, his favorite horse stolen. Halfway back, he waved down the approaching posse headed by the marshal, Jim Clark. Clark was as big and burly a man as Nunn was small. Slowing to a trot, he reached down from his horse, grabbed the little man by the arm, and swung him up behind as if he were a child. Then the posse raced off again in pursuit.

They followed the gang's trail down into Ilium Valley and along the south fork of the San Miguel toward Ames. At Ames, the waterfalls were roaring with snowmelt, the creek overflowing its banks. The posse had to slow their horses and allow them to pick their way among boulders and tree trunks that had been washed down from the mountains. The horses were winded and lathered, but the riders gave them no respite, turning them instead up the steep mountainside to gain the road to Rico.

When they reached the road, they found three horses ground-tied. Nunn's prized gelding was not among them. There was evidence that other horses had been tied there, fresh mounts, waiting. The posse pushed on, knowing that its chances of catching up with Cassidy and his accomplices had dropped from slim to none. Halfway to Rico, they discovered three more horses grazing beside the road, the stains of their sweat dried, the lather crusted. Nunn's horse was not one of them.

The marshal reined his horse in and told the men there was no point in going on. Nunn slipped off the big man's horse, and it seemed as if he was ready to go it alone again, even if it meant he would have to ride one of the gang's spent mounts bareback. Then he kicked a clod of dirt with unrestrained fury, swore, and accepted Jim Clark's help to swing back up behind him and ride back to town.

Soon after that, Nunn sold the bank and went to work as manager of the Gold King Mine, which was experiencing severe financial difficulties. The problem was costs. With coal at forty dollars a ton, operating expenses were as much as three thousand dollars per month, which made it prohibitive to mine any but the very highest-grade ore. Burning timber, which was becoming scarcer by the day, was even more expensive than coal as a source for the steam power that the mine required. A cheaper source of energy was needed. Nunn wrestled with the problem as the Gold King continued to run in the red. He pored over current and past assay reports and was both impressed and dismayed by the amount of ore available at the mine that contained good, but not good enough, quantities of gold and other minerals.

At a social event, Nunn met a visiting Serb scientist named Nicola Tesla. In the course of conversation, Tesla mentioned work that was being done with man-made electricity. He spoke of Thomas Edison, whose name was fast becoming familiar throughout the world and, before the evening was over, Nunn had a plan. He asked Tesla, as the scientist was leaving the soiree, if he would take a ride with him the next day to Ames.

Although the falls at Ames was not flowing with the force that it had been when Nunn rode past on the back of Jim Clark's horse, it was, nonetheless, impressive to Tesla. He readily agreed that if the power of the falls could somehow be harnessed, transformed, it could prove an abundant source of energy. The two men began to work up ideas. They enlisted engineering students and recent graduates from Cornell University, where Tesla taught, and they gladly flocked to the wild beauty of Telluride in return for room and board. They called themselves Pin Heads. Nunn and Tesla also had the good fortune to meet a man named George Westinghouse, who had formerly worked with Edison and now vied against him. Westinghouse believed that another form of electricity, one that he called alternating current, as opposed to Edison's direct current, would be able to transmit more voltage more easily and cheaply. The three men, along with the Pin Heads, set to work in earnest, and within a year, they had engineered the means to trap the energy of the falls at Ames and to produce alternating current electricity from it.

The discovery was an important one, and Nunn, in particular, was not timid about promoting its advantages over Edison's direct current electricity. Edison, in turn, scorned alternating current as being too volatile, too dangerous, and a poor substitute, at best, for his electricity. Their skirmishing was carried out in newspapers and at public speeches. Edison ran full-page ads warning against the dangers of alternating current. As a result, Nunn found that the investors he required to back a power plant in Ames had no confidence in his scheme.

Never one to give up easily, Nunn hit upon the idea of challenging Edison to a live demonstration of the safety of alternating current and, gambler that he was, added a ten thousand dollar wager, as a kicker, that he could prove his electricity to be safer than Edison's. Edison accepted the challenge. Nunn then borrowed the ten thousand in ten-dollar gold coins from the reserves of his former bank, pledging all of his real estate to secure the loan. Then he went with Tesla and Westinghouse to Pittsburgh for the demonstration. Their triumph there was a resounding one. Tesla served as guinea pig and chief attraction by allowing a charge of electricity to actually pass through his body like a bolt of lightening. To Edison's supreme disappointment, the Serb did not drop dead on the spot or even show signs of discomfort. Photographers captured the dramatic moment and the picture was circulated around the world. Almost immediately, Nunn had all the backing he needed to build his plant. His Cornell Pin Heads were soon putting up poles, climbing them, stringing wires, inventing arresters, and doing shop work in metal and wood, wiring, and insulation. After months of work and not a few setbacks, Nunn was ready. Before an eager crowd, he threw a switch at the plant and an arc of high-voltage, alternating current electricity jumped six feet through the air, then traveled along a power line for three miles to the Gold King Mine, where it powered a one hundred horsepower engine.

Once full power was running from Ames, costs at the Gold King dropped to just five hundred dollars per month. Suddenly, low-grade ore, discarded or ignored because of the cost of removing its impurities, could be profitably mined and processed. The Gold King was soon in the black. L.L. Nunn was credited with the first-ever long distance transmission of alternating current electricity and his wealth grew ever larger, especially as every mine owner in Telluride, and the town itself, clamored for service from his power company.

Lulled by his memories and the somnolent motion of the train, Waggoner continued to drift in and out of uneven sleep. Images and remembrances of Telluride's past welled up from his unconscious in a sometimes broken and discordant manner. He thought of Otto Mears, a man not much physically bigger than Nunn, but just as tireless. In 1891, the same year as Nunn's transmission of power from Ames to Alta, Mears completed the last length of the Rio Grande Southern railway, connecting Telluride to Durango and to the rest of the outside world. No longer were oxen required to haul Telluride's ore to the smelters in Durango and Alamosa, a distance of hundreds of miles. It was as important a development for mining cost savings as Nunn's alternating current electricity, and it cleared the way for Telluride to enter a gilded age.

Waggoner's thoughts then turned back to Jim Clark, who was assassinated a year before Waggoner's arrival as he crossed Colorado Avenue at midnight with a character known as Mexican Sam. As with the story of L.L. Nunn giving feckless chase to Butch Cassidy, Waggoner had heard the tale of Jim Clark often, but never too often.

Clark's real name was James Cummings. During the War Between the States, he joined William Quantrill's notorious guerillas on the side of the Confederacy. He became one of Quantrill's most trusted officers and gained a reputation as a gunman and killer. After the Civil War, he rode with the Younger and James gangs, made up of fellow guerillas, robbing banks and holding up trains. When the outlaw gangs broke up, Clark drifted into Leadville, where he got a job in the mines. He liked the hard physical work, as it kept him in top shape. In Leadville, he won a one hundred dollar bet for staying on his feet for five minutes with a champion heavyweight boxer. In 1887, he came to Telluride. The town was at its height of wild lawlessness, and the town council was at a loss as how to pacify and civilize it. Clark went to the council and pledged to clean things up if it would appoint him as a deputy. With nothing to lose, and impressed by the sheer bulk and obvious physical might of the man, the council agreed.

And clean the town up, Clark did. With a Winchester strategically placed for ready access in each of four stores on Colorado Avenue, and two six-shooters and a billy stick on his person, Clark beat, shot, and manhandled every drunk, cheat, and loud-mouthed tough who cared to cross him. The council was not entirely pleased by his methods, but it was more than satisfied with the results. Clark was promoted to marshall, an office that he held until his assassination upon walking out of the Brunswick Saloon on the corner of Spruce and Colorado.

During his tenure, the town was virtually clear of trouble, with two exceptions. One was the Butch Cassidy robbery of the San Miguel Valley Bank. Even after Clark had been dead for a year and more, Waggoner remembered lively debate about whether the marshal had been involved in the robbery or not. There were more than a few who argued vigorously that Butch Cassidy and Clark had ridden together with the Jameses and Youngers. Common sense argued that Telluride, with its no-nonsense, trigger-happy marshal, would not have been a likely choice for a first bank job, unless, of course, the law had been in cahoots with the outlaw. As far as Waggoner could remember, the debate was never resolved, although most people tended not to give Clark the benefit of their doubt — even less so after he died.

There had been, for a period of several months prior, reports by miners of being held-up on their way into town from the mine works at the eastern end of the canyon. The holdups were always at night and, generally, on Fridays and Saturdays when the miners were carrying their pay to town. They might also have some high-grade flake and dust that they had spirited away in the grease of their hair or matted into their beards. The description they gave of the highwayman was always the same: He was tall with a long black beard and dressed in a full-length, black oilskin slicker and a tall black hat. The marshal duly investigated the incidents but no suspect was ever apprehended.

Following Clark's death, which popular suspicion attributed to a professional marksman hired by the council to rid the town of Clark's increasing heavy-handedness, his cabin was emptied and a loose floorboard was discovered. Underneath the board, in a hollowed-out recess dug into the dirt, was a box. Inside the box was a false beard, a tall black hat, and a long black slicker.

As a young man newly arrived in town, Waggoner had loved nothing more than to listen to tales of Telluride's earlier days. Now, as he lay in the dark compartment of the train, still unable to find sound sleep, he pinched his eyes shut and rubbed them tiredly. Little did he ever think in those days that people would one day tell tales of him, that he would make bigger headlines, and more of them, than any of Telluride's colorful gallery of rogues and notables. It was not a thought that comforted him, but it was the last he had before finally achieving real sleep.

CHAPTER FOURTEEN

Grant McFerson stood at the door of the First National Bank of Delta that he had, the day before, locked. A sign hung in the door's window, advising that the bank would remain closed by his order until further notice. He watched as the life of the town went on outside. Occasionally, someone would stop to read the notice and, invariably, they shook their head before moving on. One or two bank customers, inattentive to the sign's message, had pulled on the door fully expecting it to open. One of them, after reading the sign, had kicked the door viciously and then pounded on it for long minutes before finally giving up in wrathful contempt.

The day before had been nightmarish. With some of his best people already tied up in Telluride, McFerson, upon news of Hillman's suicide, had taken it upon himself to drop everything and catch the first available train to Delta with two examiners that he had to pull from another job. They arrived to an unruly mob that had gathered at the bank, intent on withdrawing their savings. McFerson had already been in touch with the Delta marshal and a pair of brave, but nervous, deputies were at the bank when he arrived from the train station. The deputies were clearly uncomfortable, their fingers restless on their rifles, their eyes shifting constantly, their faces drawn with strain. The tellers were equally uneasy. Acting on McFerson's instructions, they had refused to dispense cash to anyone, but the pressure and conflict that they felt from the mob, most of whom were friends and even family, were palpable.

It was a scene that McFerson had witnessed all too often over the past few years. The number of small towns in the state, their former glories faded or entirely disappeared, for which he had been the bearer of yet more bad news, was seemingly beyond count. McFerson could actually quote the exact number, but it was one that grew with inexorable constancy and one that he could not help but disbelieve, regardless of all the facts and figures at his disposal. His charge as the state banking commissioner was to safeguard Colorado's banking system as a whole. He had so far been able to accomplish that, but it came at the cost of far too many individual losses and bank closures. Success had also been achieved in the face of more than a few tragedies. The suicide of Walter Hillman was just such a case, and the awful, shocking finality of it had no doubt fueled the Delta mob with even more desperation than normal.

The facts of the Delta case were far from clear, but Walter Hillman was one of the town's own, born and bred, a young man known, respected, and well liked. McFerson had personally met him a year or so previous and had thought him well presented and earnest. The telltale signs of something amiss were clearly in evidence as the examiners had begun their audit of the Delta bank. Whether or not Hillman was in any way responsible, McFerson could not yet begin to say. He wouldn't have guessed it, though. But then, after Waggoner's caper in Telluride, he was no longer as certain of his intuitive powers as he once was.

One thing he felt sure of, however. If there was fraud or embezzlement that had occurred at the Delta bank, then Hillman, guilty or not, would have fingers pointed at him. Corpses tended to have weak alibis, especially suicides.

In the street, a wagon rumbled by loaded high with bulging sacks of grain. The mules that pulled it were thin, almost gaunt, and the farmer was the same. McFerson considered the irony of the man's life, working himself to the bone to grow food for others while not having enough for himself, or his animals. He stroked his chin with the inside of his forefinger and wondered absently if the farmer had an account with the bank. The thought strayed to another, and he was soon lost in memories of other gaunt and haggard faces, the pleading, frightened eyes of ordinary men and women whose life savings were suddenly gone, vanished as if they had never existed. He had drawers full of letters, some of them literally stained by tears, imploring him to help, to reopen a bank or assist, somehow, in recovery of their lost funds. He didn't know why he saved them all. At first he had tried to write back, explaining that he would, of course, do all that he could, but that there could be no guaranties, that lost money was sometimes recouped through restructured loans and sale of assets, but that these methods mostly resulted in a return of just cents on the dollar. After a while it became impractical to respond. In some instances, he had not even had time to read the letters, and many of those in his drawers were still in their unopened envelopes.

McFerson was convinced that the people at the capitol, the governor and his staff, the senators and congressmen, did not understand how badly affected by hard times so many parts of the state were. They were insulated, out of touch. Certainly, there were representatives from afflicted districts who did their best to publicize their constituents' special needs and to obtain redress for their hardships. But their words and pleas went too often unheard, voices in the wilderness of competing claims for state funds and state attention.

McFerson rubbed his chin again. He wondered if he might be becoming a little undone by his job. He had been finding it increasingly hard to get to sleep at night, and upon waking in the morning, he no longer felt refreshed. More and more, the sight of someone like the farmer who had just passed sent him into a troubled reverie that left him feeling strangely dislocated. Sometimes it would take him several seconds to reorient himself and remember what he was doing or saying.

It was funny, though he could hardly afford to laugh about it, but when he first read Waggoner's letter from New York, McFerson's initial reaction had been giddiness, almost elation. The idea of the Telluride depositors being made whole at the expense of the country's richest banks did not displease him at all. He chided himself for sentimentality and jejune romanticism, but he couldn't help secretly cheering the shy, softly spoken banker whom he had known for many years. Now, of course, the situation had devolved into a royal mess. Not nearly enough money had actually arrived in Telluride to pay all its obligations to depositors, and the lawyering to resolve claims on the money was accelerating. The bloodhound work of accurately determining exactly what monies went where, and why, how to get them back and by whom they were rightfully owned, was amounting to nothing but headaches — and, in McFerson's case, even more sleeplessness. He had never before been involved in an interbank, interstate case. The complexities, and the legal ambiguities, were unfamiliar to him. The only polestar he had for guidance was his absolute resolve to fight as hard as he could to protect the Telluride depositors.

Whatever Waggoner's true motives, and whatever fate he came to know at the hands of the federal court, McFerson pledged solemnly to himself that he would champion the rights of the Telluride bank customers to receive as much money as they could. It was not often that large and identifiable sums were in any way available in the case of most bank closures. This time there were. The fight had already begun to perfect claims on those sums. Although McFerson felt tired and inadequately experienced, he was undaunted by the inevitable ferocity of the fray. Indeed, he welcomed it. It would, he hoped, somehow vindicate him from the guilt he felt for all those letters in his drawers and all that he had not been able to do for so many honest, hard-working folks caught unaware and unprotected.

"Sir?"

He turned from the window. John Jepson, one of his top examiners, stood as if he might have been waiting there for several minutes. It was something Jepson would do. He was unassertive and almost maniacal in his respect for authority. McFerson had no doubt at all that the man had been born to be a bank examiner. He had an imperturbable temperament and the tenacity of glue. Oddly, for someone who gave no outward indication that he possessed even a modicum of imagination, he had demonstrated profound creativity and insight, time after time, in puzzling through the records of failed banks, piecing together confused jumbles of facts to present a clear picture of what had happened. He could also recognize the telltale signs of problems developing in apparently healthy banks as quickly and accurately as a bird of prey sighting movement on the ground.

"What is it, John?"

"Mr. Hillman is here to see you, sir. Walter Hillman's father."

Hillman, Sr., had been away when his son had taken his life. He had been in Denver selling cattle. McFerson felt little enthusiasm to meet him. He was on the point of asking Jepson to intercede on his behalf, to make an excuse, any excuse that would allow him to avoid what he expected would be an unhelpful and painful interview.

"Where is he?"

"In his son's office. He came to the delivery door at the back and I let him in."

"Very well," said McFerson. Just as he could not throw away the letters in his drawers, he could not defer his responsibility now to a bereaved father.

Mr. Hillman sat at his son's desk, which was neatly arranged, even meticulous. McFerson wondered if Walter had always kept it that way, or if he had tidied it in the fashion of a last ritual.

Hillman, Sr., did not look entirely out of place. He was a tall man and, though well advanced in years, still gave an appearance of considerable physical strength. His face was weathered, brown and furrowed, and it was evident that he had been a handsome man in his time before age and toil had left their marks like intricate engravature.

He wore a suit that was slightly out of style but well made, expensively tailored. McFerson knew him to be a rancher, but he had the look, as well, of a businessman.

Hillman rose to shake hands. His grip was as firm as McFerson had expected it to be, but it lacked any real vigor. His eyes, though clear and intelligent, suffered the same deficiency.

"You know," said Hillman after their introduction, "I was one of the original founders of this bank. That was back in '86. I sat on the board of directors for pretty nearly twenty years. When my son joined the bank, it felt like a natural step. He could have worked the ranch with me, but I never pressured him to do that. He loved the ranch, but I think he wanted to do something that was less solitary, you know? Something that paid him a certain sum every month and that allowed him independence. Ranching's a hard living. You can't control so many parts of it. The weather, markets, disease — you can't predict 'em and you can't count on 'em. If a cow calves at three in the morning, you have to be there — doesn't matter whether it's a blizzard or whether you're half on your deathbed with a fever. If rain doesn't come, you have to be able to keep on with fence mending and chopping wood and collecting eggs, and whatever needs doing without cursing the endless blue sky, or drowning your worries with whiskey.

"That's how my boy was raised, sir. He chose not to be a rancher, but he knew what ranching was. He was hard-working and he had grit. This country can be harsh, and I sometimes thought he was a little too tenderhearted for it, like his poor mother had been. It killed her. It wasn't sudden, like Walter, but it killed her before her time, sure enough. Now, I guess, it's taken him, and I have to question if all the sweat and sacrifice I put into making my spread was ever worth it."

He paused and massaged his brow with one of his big, strong hands. Behind his squeezed lids, McFerson knew there were tears trying to escape. He knew, too, that the rancher would not let them. Not here, not now.

"The answer," he continued, his eyes still hidden by his hand, "is yes. It has to be. God is tough, Mr. McFerson, but he's not crooked. He doesn't give you something and then steal it away for his own benefit. He gives you a particular life to live, and the people and places that fill that life are full of lessons to learn from. I don't believe in accidents, and I don't believe a person's life, or death, is without meaning. My wife taught me more about love and acceptance in our short time together than I could ever have hoped to know without her. And she touched many others the same. Her sweetness penetrated many a crusty hide in these parts, I can assure you.

"My son was heir to his mother's sensibilities, Mr. McFerson. But he wasn't delicate. He was as good a hand, and as physically hard, as any man that ever worked for me. He wasn't a man to be stymied by a bad twist of fate. If he did something wrong, even as a little boy, he would 'fess up to it and take his due. And he made mistakes, many of 'em. He was a good boy and a good man, but he could be rash like me and do and say things he regretted."

He lapsed again into silence, studying his lap. McFerson waited, knowing that the rancher was building his way to saying something that he felt it was important for him to know. He said nothing himself, felt no need to, nor what words they could be.

Mr. Hillman looked up eventually, and when he did, his eyes fixed on the commissioner's with solemn intensity. "There are only two things that I can imagine my son taking his own life for." His voice was flat, drained. "A broken heart or a broken spirit. If it was the latter, I believe the truth of that will be found in the books and records of this bank. Where once he was proud of his position here and eager to tell me about his day, he had turned sour and silent of late. Something here, or someone, I believe, turned him that way. If it was a broken heart, and that's not something he probably would have thought he could ever talk to me about, there may be someone else to whom he did confide."

Reaching into his inside jacket pocket, Hillman took out a piece of stationery. It was sharply folded, but had evidently been crumpled previously into a tight ball, the myriad wrinkles still tattooed on it.

"I found this at the cabin," he explained, "where my son died. I went there this morning as soon as I got in from Denver. I sat a long time. When I was leaving, before I lit the cabin on fire, I saw this. The wind, I guess, had pushed it into a corner. Or maybe he threw it there. No one must have noticed it when they collected Walt's body. It's a letter, or maybe just a draft of one. It's got a lot of things scratched out, as you'll see, and it seems he wrote it fast, with words missing, as if he had too much to say and not enough time or enough words to say it."

He handed the letter to McFerson. "A letter from a man to his sweetheart is about as private and personal a thing as can be. I'm not in the habit of reading what wasn't meant for me. I'm even less inclined to share such a thing with a stranger. Anything, though, that might help me get to the bottom of why I no longer have a son, I have no qualms about prying into. I don't think Walt would object."

McFerson took the letter hesitantly. This was not one that he could throw into his drawer, unopened, unread. Hillman's hand shook just a bit as he handed the letter across the desk, creating an impression for McFerson of something alive, but mortally wounded, being offered to him, the tremble of the paper like the quiver of exposed white muscle or subcutaneous flesh.

As best he could, he read Walter Hillman's words. It was not easy, both because the words had been scribbled in haste, many of them scratched out as his father had indicated, and because they were so potent with feeling. Dead men tell no lies, but those who know they are about to die are no less inclined to the truth, however painful. In his letter, Hillman's thoughts and feelings poured out in a torrent of raw, honest language. It was clear that he harbored enormous guilt and shame, but the source was unidentified, as was the intended reader. There was no salutation, no name. It was obvious, however, that the letter was written to someone specific, a woman, and that that person, whoever she was, was already privy to Hillman's agony.

The page was covered, front and back, with an erratic and unsteady script. McFerson was nearly through both sides and feared that the letter would end with no substantive clues to help unravel the mystery of why Hillman had taken his life and whether he was directly involved in any misdeeds at the bank. Then, in the last paragraph, he found the clue he had hoped for:

> *I think of you at Cañon City, alone, confined, life unalterably the same day after day and age so, so slowly overcoming you with nothing given in return, no achievement, no realization of dreams, nothing to provide new memories that you can savor, just an endless cycle of routine and boredom and uncertain expectations for the future. And yet, as bleak as I understand your life to be, I would gladly trade it for mine. For your fate is known — you are experiencing it, knowing it, right now while mine is nothing but a phantasm that delights in filling me with dread horror of what may befall me. You can look ahead and know that however bad things are, you regain your freedom at some point certain. You will one day recommence your life, make a future, despite the flaw of your past. I have no such*

certainty. Although no walls, no bars, are holding me cap-
tive, I feel every bit as imprisoned as you. And unlike your
three years, I fear my sentence is for life.

As it had begun, the letter ended abruptly. McFerson handed it back.

"I have no idea who this woman is or what the extent of her relationship with my son was. I cannot imagine that they have known each other long. I think I would have had some idea if so, but it would appear that he had taken her fully into his confidence."

McFerson nodded in agreement. "It shouldn't be hard to find her. If she's at Cañon City with a three-year sentence, she's not going anywhere soon. I can arrange to see her. Would you like to come?"

The rancher closed his eyes in meditation. "No," he said, not opening them. "I don't believe I would enjoy hearing things about my son from someone I don't know." He opened his eyes and rose to his feet. "You go. Perhaps you would be kind enough to be in touch with me afterwards."

"I will indeed," responded McFerson, taking the older man's hand in his. "My sympathies to you."

"Thank you. And mine to you. I've followed your challenges in the paper. I don't underestimate what you have been through and what remains to come your way. I would never have thought times could turn this bad. I'm only glad that my wife didn't live to see the ruination that seems to be overtaking us...glad she didn't have to survive the loss of our son."

He walked out of the office, his posture erect but his step slow. McFerson regarded his departure with a mixture of admiration and pity. He wished he could do something to ease the old man's sorrow. He wished with all his heart that order would be restored to his state and to his country, so that men like Walter Hillman, Jr., and Buck Waggoner were not driven to acts of desperation. He tried to ignore the unsettling gnaw in his gut that had become a recurrent bother.

CHAPTER FIFTEEN

Mary Waggoner and her son had maintained a strained peace for weeks. Now, as they rode together on the train to New York, the little they had been able to communicate seemed to have faded to nothing. Delos was highly scornful of his father's misdeed, however laudable his motives might seem to others. In his mind, his father's conviction was a foregone conclusion, and the idea of being a felon's son, sharing the very name of a convict, was odious to him. Almost as bad, he suspected his mother of at least some degree of complicity. She denied knowing anything, but her son knew her to be a highly intuitive person who regularly read his mind and his father's. His parents had been married for nearly thirty years, had risen and lain down together every morning and night, their only separations caused by his father's occasional business trips, the solitary walks that took him who-knows-where in the mountains, and his regular evening card games. How could she not have known at least something of what he was planning? How could she have left Telluride with him in the middle of the night with no word to anyone about why or where they were going, and not have known or at least suspected?

Delos regarded his mother as she sat opposite him, her eyes closed. A month ago, even less, he would have felt nothing but warmth toward her. He had always been a devoted and dutiful son, but his father's quiet reserve had pushed him closest to his mother. During the years that he had been away at military school, it was to his mother that he wrote letters almost daily. Now, though, he felt nothing but shame and anger. He was engaged to be married to a Denver socialite, Josephine Wolfe. Ever since the awful news about his father was printed in the papers, he had refused to be in touch with her. He could not possibly defend or excuse his father to her, and he had no intention of sharing his parent's ignominy. His fiancée's family was one of Denver's oldest. Their name was virtually synonymous with respectability. He could not imagine that they would let his name be associated with theirs now, let their daughter give up her good name for his bad one.

Mary Waggoner peeked at her son from beneath her lowered eyelids. The silence between them was easier for her to bear if she pretended to be asleep. Her son had grown into a tall and serious young man. She thought him handsome, but not in a conventional way, his forehead was too high for that, giving his face an extra lengthiness. And his nose was, perhaps, more prominent than a sculptor would choose when preparing a classic bust. She loved his face, though, just as it was. It was hard to see her little boy in it any longer, but she still had glimpses. His eyes, until recent events, still had a boyish softness, and his smile was the same shy smile that she had seen so often on him as a child. It was his father's smile. She wished desperately that she could see it now, on either of them.

She loved her husband as much as she loved her son. It was painful for her, literally physically painful, to see them become estranged. She had even gone to a doctor, before making this trip, to see if he could explain the recurring ache that had developed in her abdomen, or the occasional sudden, shooting pains that seemed to originate at the very center of her brain. He was a Kansas doctor, recommended by her sister-in-law, and unfamiliar with any of the difficulty or upheaval in her life. He pronounced her fit and fine and explained, in vague and tactful terms, that women of a certain age experienced unfamiliar feelings of all kinds, both emotional and physical. Mary had had a powerful urge to scream at him. She had wanted to shout as loudly as she could: "I know all about a 'certain age'! What I'm feeling has nothing to do with age! It has to do with my life suddenly exploding like a faulty stick of miner's dynamite. It has to do with my son suddenly hating his father and his father suddenly under arrest for robbery and fraud!" Instead, she thanked the doctor, paid the bill, and tried to persuade herself that screaming would not have been a good choice.

Delos Waggoner had planned to bring his new bride home to Telluride. He had a small house picked out to rent and his eye on a vacant lot that he hoped to be able to buy in a year or so, and then build a house. His job at the bank, working with his father, had been going well enough, even if he wasn't afforded much responsibility. He had foreseen himself one day taking over as president, and that was a satisfying vision. He had many times imagined the "sugaree" that his friends and neighbors would stage upon his return from his honeymoon with his wife. A sugaree primarily involved beer and bells, a noisy celebration with the main intent of keeping the newlyweds from getting any sleep or even getting to bed. It was a nuisance, really, but an old Telluride tradition, and one that Delos had looked forward to. He had also daydreamed of all the places he would take his wife: horseback riding to Bridal Veil Falls and into Deertail and La Junta Basins; picnicking up Bear Creek; teaching her to slide down the mountains in winter on long, wooden skis, as he had been taught as a child by Swedish and Finnish miners.

He looked at his mother and thought of his father. Nothing would ever be the same. None of his dreams would now come true. His father, in one colossally hare-brained stroke, had ruined everything. If the people of Telluride had actually received all the money, and if his father had managed to elude capture, it might have been more tolerable — but only by a little. Instead, no funds, other than the released collateral, had made their way to Telluride, and even those were now in the hands of the commissioner, McFerson, and not the depositors. Worst of all, his father had been apprehended as easily as an engorged snake after raiding a henhouse. Why in the Devil's name, Delos wondered, had his father been at a gambling resort, registered under his own name, when he should have been hiding out in Canada or Mexico? Not only was he a crook, but he was a bungling and inept one. And now he was in custody, escorted to New York by two armed federal agents with all the dignity of a rustler or a murderer. Delos felt no sympathy for his father, nor any remorse for having none. If he had not been subpoenaed to come to the trial, he would not be on this train now with his mother. He would see his father because he had to, but he would not speak to him. After the trial, he hoped never to see him again.

Two days before they left Telluride in the Studebaker, when her husband had told her that they were making an unexpected trip to

Kansas, and that he was going on from there to New York, Waggoner had asked his wife not to ask him questions. It would be better for her, he had said, not to know too many answers. "The bank is in trouble," he had told her. "I hope to be able to fix things. It may take a while." He told her that she should bring with her any personal items, such as photos and jewelry, that had special significance, as the duration of their absence from home could extend for some time. He asked her specifically to bring the five signet rings, the hair comb, and the cigarette case that had all been made from gold dust, flake, and nuggets that their son and niece had scavenged as children from beneath the Colorado Avenue boardwalk. Not that she could have possibly left them behind. They were prized by her as much as they were by her husband.

Mary recalled with perfect clarity that summer day when the children had come running into the house, their eyes wide and manic grins on their faces. "Mama, Mama, look!" her son had shouted, leading his cousin, the pair laughing and careening through the house to the back garden like two bouncing rocks dislodged from the red cliff band above town. Her son was naked from the waist up and he was streaked with dirt. He held out his shirt that was balled like a vagabond's bundle. "Look!" he cried again, his cousin nodding her head so hard and fast that Mary wasn't sure the child's thin neck would bear the force.

She stood up from her gardening and took the proffered shirt, noting that it was, if anything, even dirtier than her child. Carefully, the children watching as if the secret of the universe was wrapped inside, she loosened the shirt. She prepared herself for what she suspected would be a snake or a spider and made ready to scream, although she was actually not scared of either. As a schoolteacher, she knew all about children's tricks and how to go along with them.

At first she saw nothing inside the shirt but what looked to be dirt and pebbles. She wondered if some small creature, suitably diabolical, might be burrowed inside. She pulled the shirt tauter and angled it out of her shadow. The small mound of dirt and pebbles suddenly came to life. It glowed in the sunlight and winked at her with yellow prismatic effect.

She looked at the children with her mouth open.

"It's gold, Mama! Gold! We found it. It doesn't belong to anyone. It's ours." Her niece's nods resumed with vigor.

"Where did you find it?"

"Underneath the boardwalk. We were playing hide-n-seek, and we found it. It wasn't just in one spot. There was a little here and a little there. Mostly it was in front of the saloons. We can keep it, can't we, Mama?" The nodding head was still again and four young eyes fixed on hers.

Mary wasn't sure what to say. If the gold did belong to someone, she would certainly want the children to return it. How they might go about discovering the rightful owner, she had no idea. A notice in the *Journal* would bring people running, she had no doubt. She could imagine the look she would get from Dad Painter for even contemplating it.

"Let's ask your father tonight when he comes home," she suggested. "He'll know what to do, I'm sure."

The bright expectation faded from the four eyes.

"You know," she added. "If the gold does belong to someone who lost it, there might be a reward."

The cousins looked at each other, uncertain if this should be accepted as good news or just not quite such bad news. They nodded then, with none of their former enthusiasm, and, for the rest of the afternoon, they waited impatiently for Waggoner, Sr., to come home, arguing one way and then another over what they thought he would say. In the end, they need not have fretted. The banker opined that the gold undoubtedly belonged to any number of miners, shaken out of the pouches in which they carried it hanging from their belts as they stumbled out of saloons and gambling halls, or were thrown out or rolled out from a tangle of brawling bodies.

"So we can keep it?" asked his son.

His father smiled and nodded. "I'll open up a safety box at the bank. I'll put it in both your names. You can come to look at it whenever you want to, but you can't take it out until you're older."

"How much is it?" asked Waggoner's niece. "In money?"

Waggoner arched his slight brows and pursed his lips. "Hard to say," he answered. "Perhaps we should take it to Henry Baisch. He's got as good an eye for high-grade as any and a little ball mill and crusher to process it."

This was received by the two children with almost as much celebration as the news that they could keep the gold. Henry Baisch was a jeweler and druggist and one of Waggoner's card partners. Anytime the two cousins went to his shop, they were given a special piece of imported candy that could be sucked for almost half an hour before its incomparable sweetness dissolved.

For the rest of that summer and in the summers that came, Delos and his cousin scoured the dirt beneath the boardwalk almost daily. In time, they had a significant collection of flake and dust. Eventually, the old boardwalk had been torn apart and replaced, mining times in town had tamed, with fewer miners and less high-grading, and Delos had become as interested in girls as in gold. The cousins split their hoard in half: Delos had the rings, comb, and case made from his share. The comb he gave to his mother, the rings to his father. The cigarette case he saved to give to someone he didn't yet know or for himself when he was older. A gold cigarette case seemed, somehow, to symbolize a great deal, and he was loathe to part with it. His mother kept all of the pieces locked safely in her jewelry box, and gradually he had asked less and less frequently to admire them.

※ ※ ※

Delos Waggoner tried not to think of his father, but was unsuccessful. His mind quested endlessly to reconcile the current abhorrent circumstances with the man he had known growing up. He had to admit that this, though by far the worst, was not the first time he had been surprised by his parent. He remembered photos that his father had commissioned for advertisements for the bank. One was of Waggoner, Sr., standing with his lieutenant, W.J. Scanlon; Scanlon posed in a decidedly cocky and aggressive attitude, while Waggoner was partially obscured behind him. In the foreground was fifty thousand dollars of gold and silver coins stacked in gleaming rows. The coins were regularly on display at the bank in those days, testimony to its financial health. Also pictured in the photograph was a brace of large Colt six-shooters, placed handily, as if ready to use, next to the stacked coins. To Delos, the guns were more interesting, more impressive, than the coins. He asked his father if he had ever had to use them.

"Oh, I've pointed them once or twice," his father replied, "but I've never had to pull the trigger." Delos was ten then, and the idea of his father holding the giant pistols in his small hands and pointing them at someone was astounding to him. He had never even heard his father raise his voice.

"Would you if you had to?"

His father nodded without pausing to think. "I believe I would."

Delos remembered with clarity the shock of that response. He tried to picture his father not merely holding the guns, but firing them, sending their bullets into a man's chest or neck or head from close range. The image was such an incongruous one that he came to believe that he had dreamed it, and that his father had never actually uttered such words.

When he was even younger, perhaps five or six, his father had taken him on a business outing to the Tomboy Mine in Savage Basin. They drove in the car of a prospective bank customer whose connections with the mine, and with his father, Delos had been unable to grasp. The man was from out of town. His name was Johnson. He was large, with jowls like a hound's, and expensively dressed in a linen suit and stiff-collared shirt that was almost startlingly white. His car was a brand new Rolls Royce, one of the few motor vehicles made that had the power and clearance to negotiate the rugged Tomboy Road. The finest car in Telluride at that time, and one of the few that existed there at all, belonged to Delos's Great Uncle James. It was a Packard. Sitting in the Rolls with his father and Johnson, Delos decided that it was almost as fine as the Packard. Perhaps, since it could drive up the Tomboy Road, which his great uncle's car could not, it was even finer.

Johnson drove at a rate of speed that made Delos afraid. His father seemed to share his sentiment, a look of near-panic etched on his face, his fingers white from the pressure of his grip on the edge of his seat. Delos remembered thinking how different his father and the business-man were. Johnson was big, relaxed, and rather loud, a tailored arm resting casually out the open car window. The large cigar between his pudgy fingers punctuated the air as he spoke; his other arm was draped nonchalantly over the steering wheel as if he was driving down a wide-open country lane rather than up a tight, steep, rutted track that had been dramatically hacked and dynamited into the ribs of the mountains. His father was everything the businessman was not. He was small, nervous, quiet, and his suit was old. He had dropped the cigar that the businessman had given him out the window at an early near-collision with a string of donkeys that had appeared suddenly in the middle of the road around a blind switchback. The surprise was that the businessman was so deferential to his father. Whatever the two were talking about, and Delos paid little attention and understood it even less, it seemed that the big man was intent on impressing his father and pleasing him. It was a perception that came clearly to Delos, but not one that he could have then articulated. It seemed clear to him, however, in a way that it never had before, that his father was an important person.

About halfway to Tomboy, on a particularly steep and twisting portion of the road, another car was encountered coming down. It was a Ford Model-T. The rule was that the car coming up had the right of way. Backing downhill was a dangerous endeavor, especially as the brakes on the early automobiles were not always reliable. Passing spots had been widened in the road every half-mile or so. Unfortunately, the Rolls had passed one just a hundred yards or so prior. For the Ford to reverse all the way to the next one up represented a delay that the businessman did not care to suffer. He stopped his car, pulled the parking brake, and jumped out with surprising agility to march toward the other driver.

"Hullo," he called out. "How much d'you pay for your car?"

"Three hundred," called back the Ford's driver. "Just bought her last week."

"She's a beauty. Tell you what. I'll give you four hundred cash for it right now."

The other driver looked puzzled but was unprepared to let such a bargain slip past him.

"She's all yours," he shouted and jumped out of the car, holding the door open and gesturing the big man to take over. Delos and his father looked at each other but said nothing.

Johnson peeled four hundred dollar notes from a large roll, handed them to the surprised owner, and then wedged himself carefully into the Ford's front seat that was substantially less accommodating than that of the Rolls Royce. He quickly backed the car up the hill no more than several yards, then stopped and turned the steering wheel hard, so that the front wheels pointed to the outside edge of the road and the steep rocky drop-off beyond. Then he clambered out, reached back inside the car to release the brake, and, with a push, sent the car rolling to its demise. Delos stared wide-eyed as the Model-T's front tires cleared the edge and its underside scraped loudly against it. Then the back of the car tipped up and over and, with a colossal din of metal smashing against rock and glass shattering, the car tumbled end over end, knocking over small trees that clung to the precipitous mountainside and bouncing off of bigger ones. Before the car had ended its careening and noisy descent, Johnson was back in the Rolls and had put it into gear to continue the climb to Tomboy.

❋ ❋ ❋

Mary thought of Telluride and her life there. She hated to think of having to give either of them up. Or of trying to go back to them if her husband, as seemed likely, was unable to return with her. She also dreaded the idea of sitting in a New York courtroom, friends and neighbors there by force of law and through no fault of their own, their eyes invariably shifting to her until she would glance back, their whispered comments perhaps inaudible to her, perhaps not. She sighed and determined that she would keep her eyes straight ahead during the proceedings and close her ears to any untoward remarks. Most importantly, she would follow her husband wherever he was bound. She had married him, "for better or for worse." After the many good years that they had enjoyed together, she would not abandon him, whatever his fate. She only hoped that her commitment to her husband would not cause her to be forever estranged from her son.

CHAPTER SIXTEEN

The Cañon City warden had summoned Anise Koen to his office to alert her that Grant McFerson, the banking commissioner, would be paying her a visit. Anise was unaware of any reason McFerson might have to call on her — unless, she reasoned, it had something to do with C.D. Waggoner and the Bank of Telluride. She feared McFerson's effort would be for naught. The banker had arranged her bond when she was elected assistant treasurer and, subsequently, so she understood from her mother, had also arranged its payment. Apart from having been a customer of the bank, both personally and on behalf of the county, she had no particular information about it or its current problems that could possibly be of help. Even if she had, she wondered if she would divulge it. Her short time in jail had jaded her. She found it very difficult in the dull state of mind induced by prison conditions to have anyone's interests at heart but her own. With the exception, perhaps, of Walter Hillman. He was the one person that she found herself thinking of often, and sympathetically.

If there was one thing that Anise had enough of in prison, it was time to think. She found that the most effective way to banish the very dark thoughts that regularly tried to press into her consciousness, leaving her empty and hopeless and as alone as if she were stranded on a rock surrounded by tempest seas, was to picture Walter and to fantasize about a life together with him. When her sentence was over, she would still be a young woman, still perfectly able to bear children and enjoy a normal family life. Prison life had thus far taken a physical as well as emotional toll, but, she reasoned, if she set herself to it she could mitigate, if not completely stop, the ravages of too little fresh air and sunlight, too much sleeplessness and stodgy food. She would eat less, she pledged herself, and more selectively. She would be the first in line to go outdoors every day, regardless of the weather, and the last in line to come back inside. Rather than lie for hours trying to fight her way to sleep, she would take up a hobby, such as writing or drawing, and advantage herself of the quiet at night to allow inspiration to come to her.

What gave her most hope of late was knowing that Walter's feelings for her were not, would never be, shaded by what she had done. He had accepted her already for who she was, her criminal record no more an apparent impediment to his feelings than the weather or the time of day. She would need to keep no secret from him about her past. That thought was delicious to her, and she savored it long and often. Although she knew that it might be dangerous, a risk of disappointment and letdown, she allowed herself, encouraged herself, to imagine marrying Walter. She filled in the details of where they would live, which state or even country, and what their house would look like. She named their children, two boys and a girl, and gave them nicknames. She imagined evenings alone by the fire when the children were asleep, reading to him from her essays and stories or asking his opinion of her sketches. She saw herself embraced by him, pulled tightly to him, feeling the strength of his manhood, yielding to it.

She worried, too, about his problems at the bank. She had written to him just that day to tell him that they did not matter. Nothing mattered but that they be together as soon as they could. She encouraged him to be open and honest, even if it meant shame or worse.

> *Nothing, my dearest friend,* she had written, *nothing can be so bad that it should hinder the good that will come to us. Be brave and strong and know that I know and accept with all my heart what you have done. It is nothing worse than what I and too many others to count have done before us and will continue to do. We are human. We make mistakes. But, as humans, we also have the power to redeem ourselves and to turn our unhappiness to joy. Do not be afraid, Sweet One, of those who wield authority. Your only judge is God, and He, I know, forgives you. All that is left is to forgive yourself and to save yourself for me.*

She wondered how quickly her letter would reach him and how speedily his reply would come back to her. She clutched at a sudden thought: perhaps she could intercede on his behalf. Maybe in the course of her meeting with McFerson, who was due at any moment, she could explain Walter's circumstances and appeal to the commissioner for help. As immediately as it had come, the thought fled. She didn't know, had no way of knowing, any of the real details surrounding Walter's case. Perhaps his problems would resolve themselves. Perhaps the worst possible thing she could do would be to alert McFerson to something about which he might have no idea.

How she wished she could see her friend, hold his hands in hers, whisper to him her love.

A shadow fell across her as she sat lost in thought. She looked to the barred door of her cell and saw a stranger there in the company of a guard. It was McFerson. He was a handsome man, his face a kind one. The look in his eyes, though, was not at all what she had been expecting.

※ ※ ※

The hotel that Alta Cassietto had chosen was within a few blocks of the courthouse where C.D. Waggoner was to be tried. She had looked into three different hotels before making her choice. She felt like Goldilocks testing the porridge, the chairs, and the beds in the home of the three bears. Like the fairy-tale child, she felt she had made just the right choice. The hotel was not the most expensive, nor the cheapest of the three. Neither was it the biggest, or the smallest. It was not the busiest, the cleanest, the quietest, or the most well known. It was, however, at least to her mind, the most completely New York. It had a style that was subdued, refined, but not at all stuffy. There were fresh flowers in the lobby and in the rooms and original contemporary art in the hallways. Her room was small and tastefully appointed. Her canopy bed was covered with a satin duvet and her linen sheets were changed and pressed every day. There was a small but entirely adequate Queen Anne writing desk, and she sat at it each morning and evening to pen her articles and thoughts. The room seemed made for writing, and she was pleased with the ease with which she was able to fill her pages.

The hotel served high tea at four in the afternoon and, for breakfast, provided wonderfully fresh bread and scones with rich, dark, fruit conserves and butter sculpted into scallop-shell shapes. Alta had not yet missed either breakfast or tea. What delighted her the most was that they were included in the price of her room. She felt as if she was more than getting her money's worth. She sent Dad Painter a post card showing the hotel lit softly at night.

Alta had come to New York several days prior to the date set for the trial. She had spent her time visiting the offices of different newspapers and meeting reporters who had been covering the Waggoner story. There seemed to be quite a sharp delineation between those who were prone to portray the banker as a hero and those who simply thought him a crook. For the most part, the divide seemed to correspond to regional geography, with western reporters falling in the first camp and eastern ones in the latter. A rare exception was Nick Alexander, who wrote a column for the *New York Sun* called "Nick 'o Time," which offered commentary on topical, social, and political issues and that was, daily, wryly humorous and insightful. So far, Alexander had refrained from either congratulatory words or contumely in his pieces. The *Sun* had been one of Alta's first calls. Alexander had not been there, but she was told that he was the right person for her to meet. In the afternoon when she returned, he was at his desk, which was entirely covered in writing pads, books, and newspapers. He was on the phone with his back turned to her. She stood waiting, not wanting to presume by sitting, and not caring, but being unable to help, to be in a position to overhear his conversation.

Whoever was on the other end of the telephone line had been dominating the conversation for the past minute. Alexander nodded and shook his head and ran his fingers through the thick waves of blond hair at the back of his head. Suddenly he spun his chair around.

"That's complete bull!" he said. Noticing Alta, he amended what he was about to say. "Baloney," he said. "Complete and utter baloney. And if you're buying it, you're as cowed by that puffed-up politico as the rest of your editorial staff. I gotta go. Call you later."

He hung the mouthpiece in its hanger and smiled at Alta as if he had all the time in the world and few concerns. He had brown eyes and a full head of sand-colored hair. His nose was slightly crooked, off-center, as if it had once been broken, and a thin, faint scar traced a jagged pattern for an inch or so underneath his right eye. He looked to be in his mid-thirties, and he had an air of being utterly confident but not cocky. This served to distinguish him from many of the other newspapermen that Alta had met in New York.

"Hello," he said, rising. "I'm Nick Alexander. How can I help you?"

Alta noticed approvingly that he did not thrust his hand out to be shaken. It was one of her pet peeves that so many men didn't observe a woman's discretion in shaking hands, didn't wait to see if the woman offered hers first.

She put out her hand and introduced herself.

"Alta? That's an unusual name. In Spanish that means 'tall,' doesn't it? Did your parents think it was a name you would grow into?" His smile was about as beguiling as any Alta had ever encountered.

She laughed. "No. If you must know, I'm named after a gold mine."

"A gold mine?" Alexander whistled. "Let me guess. You're from Telluride and you're here to see me about C.D. Waggoner."

"Is that reporter's intuition, clairvoyance, or were you told I had been here earlier?"

It was Alexander's turn to laugh. "It's important for a reporter to keep his sources secret, don't you think? Please, sit down. I would love to talk to you about Mr. Waggoner. I consider his story one of the most fascinating human-interest pieces in the news right now. The problem is, I don't really know what the story is. So, I was actually hoping you could help me. So far I've had to stick pretty closely to the facts as reported by the banks and the commissioner in Colorado — McFerguson or MacFarley..."

"McFerson."

Alexander snapped his fingers and treated her with another smile. "Listen," he said, leaning forward over the stacks of papers and books as if he were conspiring with her. "I'm on a too-tight deadline right now. But..." he glanced at his pocket watch, "I should be done by six or thereabouts. What say we go to dinner and talk about your fellow Telluridian? Do you have plans, or can I call for you at your hotel?"

"I'd be happy to go to dinner," said Alta, proud of herself for not hesitating. She was not accustomed to dining with men whom she had never before met. But then, she was not usually in New York, and she had no plans, and Alexander was exactly the kind of reporter, in terms of readership and influence, that she wanted to be sure had the proper impression and understanding of Telluride. As well, she could imagine worse company. Her only worry was whether she would be able to concentrate on anything other than his smile, crooked nose, and the small, spidery scar.

"Great. It's settled then. Where are you staying?"

"The Palmyra Hotel. Do you know it?"

"Absolutely. Just near the courthouse, isn't it? Sort of chic, arty, but no baloney? Great teas in the afternoon?"

"That's it. To a tee." Alta now glanced at her watch. "Speaking of which," she said, getting up, "it's almost teatime now. I've promised myself I wouldn't miss one while I was staying there. I'm not saying that Telluride isn't civilized, but I think the last time anyone served high tea there was around the time that William Jennings Bryan made his speech in front of the Sheridan Hotel."

"1906?"

"1903, actually."

Alexander snapped his fingers again. "Never was keen on memorizing dates. But I won't forget ours. Pick you up at, say, seven. Deal?"

"Deal. I'll look forward to it." She put out her hand again and Alexander brought it to his lips. Like high tea, it was a gesture rarely experienced anymore. The reporter affected it with easy grace. Alta was charmed.

�ంక ✦ ✦

Nick Alexander's manners at dinner were as impeccable as they had been at his office. There was nothing at all stiff about him, though. Somehow, he managed to be casual while being completely proper. He was evidently very well brought up, but Alta had no luck pressing him for details of his past. His only interest was learning about Telluride, and understanding what light she could shed on C.D. Waggoner's heist, which he had headlined in a column as "the almost perfect crime."

"Obviously, the question becomes: is he a latter-day Dick Turpin, a Robin Hood? Or are things murkier? Is your Mr. Waggoner a good egg or a bad apple?"

Alta paused, her spoon halfway from her soup. "Will I be quoted?"

Alexander laughed and held up his hands. "I'm not writing this down. But I will consider you a reliable source."

She savored the spoonful of soup. It was a rich, creamy bisque, the perfect complement, she thought, to the brisk autumn evening.

"If you had asked me a month ago, or anyone in Telluride, it would not have been a question even worth posing. Buck Waggoner may be the best-known person in town. The Bank of Telluride is the only bank in town, and he's been there for over thirty years."

"A kind of country doctor figure?"

"Exactly. Anything to do with money in Telluride, or lack thereof, invariably involves Buck Waggoner. And it's been that way for years."

"Well, he certainly seems to be involved with the lack thereof at the moment. And not just in Telluride. Do you know," Alexander leaned toward her as he had at the office, his eyes full of almost child-like excitement, "I was speaking to our legal affairs people, and they predict that the wrangling between attorneys and with your state banking commissioner will drag out endlessly. Not just about Waggoner and his guilt or innocence. There's half a million dollars that has, effectively, gone astray. And regardless of whether it's all fully located and accounted for, the question of ownership, of who has or hasn't rights to it, is likely going to prove a real legal conundrum."

"But surely it belongs to the banks it was taken from. I would prefer nothing more than for the Bank of Telluride depositors to be able to get their money, but common sense and logic tell me that money fraudulently obtained still belongs to the defrauded parties."

"Two things to remember, though," cautioned Alexander. "First is the nine-tenths rule of possession. The New York banks do not have the cash. At least, not all of it. Waggoner apparently repaid some notes with part of it, and so they have that cash. But when the notes were repaid, collateral that they had held to secure the notes was released and returned to Telluride — cash, and notes, and mortgages convertible to cash. The rest of the money was apparently sent hither and yon to various other banks, but it was always for credit to the Bank of Telluride. All that money is potentially up for grabs, and Mr. McFerson, rightly so, is apparently not the type of person to easily relinquish any possible claim that he can assert.

"The second thing is, Waggoner consummated the transfers of funds by presenting properly signed and certified drafts."

He looked at Alta as if she could finish his thought. She felt the heat of blood rising in her face. "I have no idea what that actually means," she confessed, and, perceiving no smug hauteur in Alexander's eyes, she felt her flush as quickly recede.

"It means that a fundamental component of our banking system, a cornerstone, is going on trial with Waggoner."

"And that is to do with...?"

"That is to do with the sanctity, the inviolability, of a bank's certification. When a draft is presented to a bank, it is a demand to pay the presenting party whatever amount the draft is made for. If the bank on whom the demand is made certifies the draft, it guaranties payment.

A certified draft on a bank is as close as you can come to holding actual cash. Do you follow?"

Alta nodded and sipped at her water. Alexander took a moment to cut the prime rib beef that had been served him while he spoke and to take a few mouthfuls. Alta had ordered cod. As she cut through its golden breadcrumb coating, she felt as if she were not just thousands of miles from Telluride, but a whole world and lifetime away. There simply were not any bright, single, young men like Nick Alexander in her town, and although seafood was available, it was certainly not fresh. She would never have guessed it could happen, but she was actually happy to be away from Telluride.

"So," Alexander went on, "if the bank that certified those drafts, which happens to be one of the oldest, biggest banks in the country, now turns around and says that its certification is invalid, that it doesn't stand by its own promise that the drafted funds are good and available ones, it threatens to throw the whole banking system into upheaval."

He reached under the table and pulled up his worn leather satchel. From it he extracted a newspaper. "The cartoonists have had a field day with this case." He folded the paper open to the funnies page and handed it across the table. Alta smiled at the caricature of Buck Waggoner, dwarfed by a tall cowboy hat, sauntering on Wall Street with a clutch of drafts, while a cadre of portly bankers ran for cover and hid trembling.

"Whether or not Waggoner knew what an intricate mess he would create, I don't know," he said, taking back the paper. "If it wasn't planned, he couldn't have done better if he had tried. If it was, then he may just be the 'dazzling financier' and 'financial genius' that some are making him out to be. What do you think?"

Alta sighed. As far as she knew, Waggoner had always been a good banker. She had certainly never heard anyone defame him for being a bad one. He had been intimately tied to Telluride's economic growth and development and to its struggle against decline. Without doubt, a high degree of competency and adroitness had been required of him. The words "dazzling" and "genius," however, were not ones that sprang to mind.

"I don't know if he foresaw all the consequences of his actions," she replied. "I don't think there is any love lost between anyone in Telluride and the New York banks. Or the Denver banks, for that matter. Our perception is that they were eager to crowd in when times were good and even more eager to pull up stakes at the first sign of a downturn."

"Well," smirked Alexander, "they are banks, after all: happy to give you an umbrella when the sun's shining but grab it back when it rains."

"A bank like the Bank of Telluride isn't that way, though. It can't be. Its stakes are not removable. Its shareholders, its depositors, its customers, and its employees all see each other every day — they live in the same small community, go to church together, have children in school together.

"I think," she said, not entirely sure that she had, as yet, completely formulated her thoughts about Waggoner and his astounding caper, "I think he was trying desperately to get out of a hole. Whether the hole had swallowed just the bank or him, personally, as well, I cannot know. Knowing the history of Telluride, it wouldn't surprise me to think that he could have had personal debts that were onerous. And I believe he was genuinely trying to save his friends and customers, even at the risk of getting caught and going to jail."

Alexander nodded, a thoughtful look on his face. "You know, I always, secretly, wanted to be a mystery writer. I love cloak-and-dagger stories, full of dark and dangerous characters. And, of course, a hero. I have been enthralled by the Waggoner story since the day it broke, and I've often thought since what a good mystery it would make. The problem is, I can't decide which side of the storyline Waggoner's on. Is he a hero, or is he a dark and dangerous character?"

Alta was careful to swallow before she laughed. "'Dark and dangerous doesn't quite fit, I'm afraid.' He's quiet and perhaps a little odd you know, eccentric. You would never notice him in a crowd. I've known him practically my whole life and have never known him to exude even a hint of darkness or danger. More likely he would be the victim in your mystery. The poor innocent who had no enemies, but winds up dead or blackmailed, or whatever happens to poor innocents in mysteries."

"Ah, but surely you know," pressed Alexander, "that the 'poor innocent' is rarely, if ever, truly innocent. There's always a story behind what happens to them. That's what intrigues me about your Mr. Waggoner. I've seen his photograph, and I concur fully that he hasn't the look of a villain. Quite the opposite. But I will wager you another dinner this week that he has something to hide."

He stuck out his hand to shake. Alta took it. "I'm not sure how we'll judge the winner," she smiled, "but if you're inviting me to dinner, I accept. How about we go Dutch?"

"You're on. The trial starts the day after tomorrow. We'll probably learn a fair amount then. Shall we dine that evening and compare notes?"

"We shall," agreed Alta. "Let the mystery unfold."

CHAPTER SEVENTEEN

The area reserved for the press in Courtroom D of the New York Federal District Courthouse had been expanded from its normal dimensions, but, even so, it was densely crowded with reporters sharing seats, kneeling and crouching between rows, and filling the aisles. Alta and Nick had made a point of arriving early but were still too late to find more than one empty seat. Nick insisted that Alta take it. When she refused steadfastly, he invited her to flip a coin. Instead, Alta prevailed on him to share the seat with her. While the arrangement was not entirely comfortable, Alta found she didn't mind it. She was so accustomed to being alone and doing things on her own, it was a pleasant change to feel allied with someone else, and with a whole corps of others. If not for the actual matter-at-hand, Alta could have truly enjoyed herself.

Her feelings, though, were necessarily tempered by the actuality of the trial. Seeing Waggoner — staring out the window as if in a trance — and his wife and son — the former never averting her eyes from her husband, the latter assiduously studying the floor, both of them perceptibly uncomfortable — took away any lightness she might have felt, replacing it with a ponderous sadness. It was sobering, as well, to see so many fellow Telluridians in the courtroom. Away from their normal surroundings, their customary clothes eschewed for new suits and dresses, she almost had trouble recognizing some of them. They seemed uniformly ill at ease, reticent, abashed by the setting and the circumstances.

"Look," said Nick, nudging her and nodding toward the front of the press section. "That's Will Rogers." Alta adjusted her position to try to make out the famous humorist.

"The one with the big ears," whispered Nick, but she could not make him out through the maze of heads in front of her. "I'll try to introduce you. I've met him a few times. He might remember me."

Alta had no doubt Rogers would remember. She had come to realize that Nick was extremely well-known and respected as a journalist.

Being with him was almost more akin to being in the news than to reporting it. Everyone seemed to want to say hello to him, shake his hand, get his take on things. She had noticed, too, more than one beautiful sophisticate eye her up and down as if in shock that Nick could be with someone so unknown and obviously small-town. Now, sharing a seat with him, exchanging whisperings, she was convinced she would see her name and perhaps even her picture in a New York gossip column the next day.

In addition to Rogers, many other luminaries were in the capacity crowd. Senators L.C. Phipps and Charles W. Waterman from Colorado were in attendance, as was U.S. Postmaster General Brown. Grant McFerson and his deputy, John Jepson, were there with their attorneys from the firm of Moynihan, Hughes, and Knousall. The New York banks were represented by H.C. Vidal of Hodges, Wilson, and Rogers. Vidal was a small and intense character with impenetrably dark eyes and a button mouth that turned down at the corners, as if he were in a constant state of disappointment. There were Wall Street potentates, Broadway stars, a small group of heavy-set and bejeweled men with shifting dark eyes who looked uncomfortable to be in such proximity to a federal judge, and dozens of ordinary people fascinated to find out the verdict on a man they felt as if they personally knew from the myriad accounts they had read in the papers.

The courtroom was a cacophony of voices when Judge Frank J. Coleman entered in his ceremonial robe. Even after the bailiff had called "Oyez, oyez," the noise subsided only slightly and occasioned the first of what would be repeated use of the judge's gavel. As she had many times since the Waggoner story first broke, Alta felt a flood of mixed emotions. This time, however, they were even stronger. It was as if she were part of a detective story that was drawing ever closer to its denouement, and now, as the pages turned faster and faster, she was at once hesitant and eager to know the outcome.

"You know," she whispered to Nick, "this is about more than one man or one crime. The fate of our town could rest on the verdict." Without wishing to, she felt herself about to cry. Her lip trembled as she held back the tears. Nick pulled a handkerchief from his pocket and tucked it into her hand. She nodded her thanks and held the piece of cloth tightly, but did not use it.

C.D. Waggoner sat with three lawyers at a long, highly polished table. Samuel Crump, from Denver, was his lead defense counsel. He was supported by Alan Campbell and Elwood Rabenold. Crump, a preeminent lawyer with a national reputation, had originally entered a plea of emotional insanity for his client. Learning of this, the government prosecutors had interceded with Judge Coleman to have Waggoner examined by a state alienist. The judge agreed and received a report back from Assistant U.S. Attorney Kleid that the alienist found the banker to be normal in every respect and of "supernormal" intelligence. The defense withdrew its plea.

The prosecution was headed by U.S. Attorney Charles H. Tuttle. He was aided by Assistant U.S. Attorney Emanuel H. Kleid. Tuttle was a slender man, fastidiously dressed, young enough to still have more blond than gray in his neatly combed hair. He wore small wire rim glasses that he had the habit of taking off and putting back on at regular intervals. In his appearance, he could easily have passed as a Wall Street banker. His shoes shone as brightly as the polished table, in stark contrast to Waggoner's, which Alta noticed were scuffed and worn and dull. Kleid, older than Tuttle by several years, was no match in appearance to the younger attorney. He was heavier, less nattily attired, his face round and large and open compared to Tuttle's narrow, ferrety features. His shoes, though not so bad as Waggoner's, were unpolished and did nothing to complement his suit.

Nick leaned toward Alta. "I've seen this fellow Tuttle in action before," he confided. "He's like one of those bred-to-fight dogs that lock their jaws when they get a good bite and then can't release them. I'm afraid your man will need either consummate good luck or divine intervention to pry himself free."

The opening statements by the opposing attorneys were markedly different. They essentially mirrored the different arguments that had been posited since Waggoner was first apprehended. For the defense, Samuel Crump, white-haired, avuncular, a pleasing resonance in his voice and a steady, soothing cadence, depicted his client as an everyman ensnared by circumstance. Desperate to save his bank and his customers, he resorted to desperate means. The attorney asked the court to look on his client's actions not so much as a crime, but as a deed of extreme and flawed judgment, an act of passion.

Samuel Crump, in his patrician demeanor, spoke informally, almost genially, as if telling an anecdotal story to a classroom of students. He directed his words, in equal part, to the judge and the audience.

"You should know," Crump began, "that this crime of which my client is accused, follows thirty-three years of labor and conscientious effort in building up a banking institution in a once-thriving mining town surrounded by prosperous stock and grazing territory. These efforts succeeded, and his bank became a monument to his industry. It was his life, and its success and its credits were his inspiration.

"During the Near Panic of 1907, when many banks closed and many more failed to pay out cash, Mr. Waggoner was able to supply urban banks with large advances of gold and maintained in certain banks generous credits. Shipments of gold and cash to these banks ran into six figures within a single month. His business with larger banks was eagerly sought and maintained. It was then a valuable asset to these corresponding institutions. The Bank of Telluride was a fine bank. Mr. Waggoner had built up deposits to $1.5 million, and his loans and discounts exceeded one million. These loans, in those good days, were considered gilt-edged assets.

"Then came along the slump of depression following the inflated wartime conditions. What had happened to other mining and stock communities also happened in San Miguel County. Good securities were not so good. Collections became hard to make. Mines were closing. Stockmen were unable to meet their obligations. There came a time when the bank, like many others, had to borrow. Some loans were obtained, others were promised but later refused. Certain parties became troublesome. Whisperings went about from mouth to mouth, and withdrawals of cash followed.

"Distrust was encountered in banking circles, touching on the solvency of Mr. Waggoner's bank. In fact, his bank was solvent, but it needed cash. The storm was gathering, and Mr. Waggoner saw trouble ahead. He became obsessed with one overwhelming purpose: to save his friends and neighbors of a third of a century from loss and possible ruin. They had trusted him all these years, and he conceived but one mission in life. The more than five hundred thousand dollars that the books showed he was personally worth did not concern him. He would sacrifice all he was, all he owned, for his depositors. He spent weeks in New York and Denver in attempts to secure loans and, in the main, his appeals were denied.

"He had secured a promise of a two hundred thousand dollar loan on all of his personal assets, conditioned on his procuring three hundred thousand dollars in life insurance. He finally secured the policy, and, after several weeks spent in an effort to consummate the deal on the loan, he met with failure. He came back to Telluride and paid in full the first year's premium on the policy. If he could ride the crest, so he thought, he could save the day."

For two hours that morning, Waggoner had refused to leave the cell where he had been detained while awaiting trial. On threat by Hugh Patton, the U.S. Marshall for New York, to use force to deliver the banker to court, and through emotive persuasion by Elwood Rabenold, Waggoner had, at last, yielded. Now, as he would throughout the trial, he sat motionless, his back to the gallery of spectators and witnesses, staring out the tall dirt-streaked window ahead of him that afforded little view, except of the building opposite. Pigeons came and went, using the outside windowsill as a roost.

There were no pigeons in Telluride, Waggoner mused as his attorney spoke plaintively of the hard times that had beset his town and his bank. There were doves and grouse, eagles, hawks, wild turkey, even hummingbirds, but no pigeons.

It was a chill gray day outside, the weather matching perfectly the dirty, drab coloration of the birds on the window ledge. Only half listening to his attorney's oration, Waggoner felt happy that he had lived so many years in a town where clearly pronounced English was often the exception to a rule of heavy accents, roughly mishandled grammar, and words for which one's ear had frequently to be more sensitive to inflection and what was unsaid than to the actual words themselves.

He recalled a day, gray and cold like this one, and a funeral service — one of a hundred or more that he attended over the years. At the eastern end of the canyon that ringed Telluride like a horseshoe, there had been an avalanche. An early and uncharacteristically warm spring day had triggered the sudden release of what the miners called "white death." A young Italian woman, a miner's wife, was outside her small cabin — more of a shack — on the lower slope of Ajax Mountain. She was hanging laundry to dry, oblivious of the huge fracture line that had suddenly and soundlessly formed as a jagged black streak across the gleaming white snow above her. At the moment of first hearing the monstrous noise of the slide — a sound that Waggoner had more than once heard and that was like none other on earth — the young woman would have had time to do nothing more than jerk her eyes up the mountain in blind panic. The noise she would have heard would have been the combination of a locomotive derailed, a hurricane, and the caterwaul of a thousand wild animals. Those sounds would have been concentrated into a single force of noise, at first muffled by the snow, until the snow would have seemed to accept that it was, itself, the noise, and, with that realization, given full vent and voice to its unalterable power. The gathered pressures of the snowslide, as they manifested themselves in an exhalation of wind so powerful that nothing standing could resist it, flung the woman a hundred feet from her cabin to safety. Then, with the precision of a papercutter, the avalanche severed her cabin, one side disappearing in an instant of fury into the maelstrom of snow and rock, splintered wood and unidentifiable debris, the other side left standing lamely, its sparse furnishings sucked out and spat back in pieces to litter what had, moments before, been an unsullied patch of snow-covered yard.

The woman had suffered a broken arm, cuts, and contusions, but no more physical injury than that. The funeral that Waggoner had attended, some days later when the early spring had vanished, relinquishing the world back to cold, colorless winter, had been for the woman's baby daughter, who had been napping in a cradle inside the cabin. No trace of the child was ever found, even after every chunk and flake of the slide's terminal slough had melted and run to join the swollen San Miguel in clear, gentle streamlets.

At the funeral, the woman and her husband stood together at the small gravestone that they had not been able to afford, but which they had purchased with fifteen dollars borrowed from the Bank of Telluride. With no body to bury, there had been no need of a grave, no tiny casket to cost the couple additionally. The husband wept openly, but the wife was silent and unmoving. Throughout the service, conducted in broken Italian and English and broken Catholic orthodoxy, the young woman, Waggoner recalled, had stood perfectly still and dry-eyed. Soon after the funeral, she returned to Italy, leaving her husband behind. He continued to work in the mines, until one day he grabbed onto an electrified cable and was scorched of life. He was buried in the Lone Tree Cemetery next to his daughter's small gravestone.

That had been in 1904, toward the end of the mining troubles. It had been a time that Waggoner had found vexing. His natural sympathies were with the hard-working miners, so many of whom were immigrants with nothing in the world to help them make their way but the strength of their hands and backs and spirits. The bank's largest customers, however, were the mine owners and their rich sympathizers. Fighting broke out between the camps — vicious, brutal fighting. There were murders on either side. Men were ambushed, dragged from their homes, shot at point blank range, or beaten and hung. Men like Bob Meldrum were hired by the owners to intimidate union organizers and to protect against their reprisals. One such avenging act took the life of Clyde Barney, a shift boss at the Smuggler-Union. One day at the beginning of winter, Barney had simply disappeared. He was not seen again until the spring, when his rotted carcass, mauled by scavenging animals and the depredations of the weather, was happened upon in the woods on Coonskin Ridge. The discovered corpse, its bones picked clean but for tufts of foul black flesh and putrefied muscle, was bound for Lone Tree Cemetery when a group of Citizens' Alliance riders, led by Bulkeley Wells, blocked its progress down Colorado Avenue.

"We mean no sacrilege," Wells announced, "but a tombstone is inadequate testimony to a martyr's cause. I want every unionist dog to know that Clyde Barney will not yet be buried and forgotten."

He gave a nod to one of the riders, who slipped from his horse and jumped onto the flatbed wagon, carrying Barney's grotesque remains. As if plucking a melon, he snatched up the dead man's skull, the black holes of its eye sockets and nasal cavity gaping in dumb, but accusing shock. Its teeth, unprotected by any skin of lips, and the gaps between them void of gum tissue, looked as if they were prepared to feast on poisonous, diabolical fare. The shift boss' unmistakable red hair still clung in places to the skull, like sprouts of virulent weed rooted desperately to hard, barren ground. At another nod from Wells, the man strode across the street, the skull carried in his hands as if it were nothing more than a purchase from the butcher's. He entered Wells' office, which served as headquarters for the Alliance, and placed the skull in the window, where it would cast its sightless stare for a week.

Like many, Waggoner had been disgusted by the display. As it had on their first night together gambling, another side of Wells had revealed itself, a violent and ruthless side. The next time Wells came to see him at the bank, Waggoner asked him if he really believed such a grisly gesture was warranted.

"Fuck, Buck," Waggoner had expostulated, though he hadn't been drinking. "Is it any more grisly to stick a man's head in a window than it is to murder him in the first place? To toss his dead body into the woods for coyotes and cougars to gnaw on? And anyway, this is not about one man or the horror of his putrid skull. This is about the whole venerable system of free enterprise. This is about the sanctity of ownership. You don't expect your housemaid to start telling you how to arrange your furniture, do you? Does your craps dealer tell you how to bet? If miners don't like the work they do or the way their mining company treats them, they can go find other work, can't they? They aren't slaves. They're hired and paid exactly as they were told at the outset of working they would be."

"But what of the Fathom System?" asked Waggoner. "That's new. Miners here have never worked under such a system before."

"So they can quit," returned Wells. "You decide to add a room to your house. Does your housemaid have the right to tell you your house is now too big and she won't clean the new room? Does your craps dealer refuse to throw the dice because he thinks he works too hard and because you're winning too much on your bets?"

Waggoner knew better than to argue. When he wanted to, Wells could be a sophist of the first order. He had been in the debate club at Harvard and had learned to argue either side of a coin toss and to flip an opposing argument on its head and spin it. When arguing about something he actually believed in, a belief he was passionate about, he relinquished no quarter.

"This is war, Charles," Wells went on. "The unionists are trying to destroy the natural order of things, and that cannot be allowed. And don't think for a minute that the agitators are fighting for anyone's interests but their own. It's power and money they want. And not for some Heinrich or O'Shaughnessy who's drilling with a widow-maker, either. They want it for themselves. And the only way they can see to get it is by taking it from those who have drawn a better hand than they have and played it smarter."

Waggoner related Wells' words to Harry Miller as the barber brushed his friend's face with hot shaving lather. Miller scoffed with derision.

"I know you like Wells," he said, "and I'm not above sitting at the poker table with him. He can be good company. He can be the action end of a jackass, too. If I wasn't worried that some two-bit goon with a gun, like that sawed-off son of a bitch Meldrum, would shoot me in the back as I walked out the door, I'd have taken Barney's head out of Wells' window already and thrown it in the trash where it belongs. 'Course, I might have had to trim those clumps of red hair first. No man, dead or alive, should ever be allowed to have his hair in such a state."

In the end, neither side had truly won or lost. The miners succeeded in organizing, but their union never grew to be as strong as they wished. If they struck, the owners had little difficulty finding scabs who were eager enough for work to brave the unionists' threats. The owners preferred not to have to resort to scabs, whose skills and experience were generally inferior, and they found themselves compromising somewhat to union demands for purposes of expediency. After the war, as prices slid and the economy weakened, the miners and the owners stared at a mutual problem of survival. Subsequently, the antagonism between them abated, but it never disappeared.

🎺 🎺 🎺

Samuel Crump finished his opening oratory, and Tuttle stood to address the court. Following the defense attorney's seasoned and professorial presentation, Tuttle seemed extremely young, ruling more by calculation than passion. The prosecutor, as intense in his manner as his opponent was relaxed, made it quickly and unmistakably clear that he ascribed to none of Crump's notions about the defendant's act. Any attempt to excuse what Waggoner had done, he argued, was an exercise in casuistry.

"Your Honor," he began, standing directly in front of the judge, his glasses off and held behind his back until they would be called again to rest briefly on his sharp, straight nose and wrap around his ears. "Your Honor, I feel the time has come to tear the mask of hypocrisy from C.D. Waggoner's unwilling face. I do not consider the defendent as a good man who has made a great personal sacrifice to save his family and friends. Rather, I consider him a scoundrel of the worst variety. Far from acting as a trusted friend and protector of his Telluride neighbors, I believe and intend to prove that he engaged for many years in fraudulent transactions that have now bankrupted both his institution and his friends. It is a case deserving of no sympathy but, instead, of severe punishment."

Putting his glasses back on, and having made no effort to address the press, the witnesses, or the general audience, Tuttle took his seat again. The brevity of his opening remarks and his brisk, unsmiling delivery contrasted starkly with Crump's style. After listening to his attorney, Waggoner had allowed himself some hope that the judge would consider his case no more than an ill-conceived misadventure and dismiss him with a light sentence. Now, hearing Tuttle, and witnessing the cold zeal of the prosecutor's delivery, his hope faded.

The host of witnesses that had been subpoenaed, most of them from Telluride, was extensive. From the Bank of Telluride were Clarence Downtain, the cashier; Delos Waggoner, the assistant cashier; W.J. Scanlon, vice president; and Miss Alice Lingren, Waggoner's personal assistant. Dora Carlson, a former bank employee who had moved to

Seattle, was also there. The prosecution contended that Waggoner had offered her one thousand dollars to send the fraudulent wires to New York. Waggoner's niece, Amelia Jones, had also been subpoenaed, as had Waggoner's sister, Mrs. C.E. Todd, and Mildred Hart and Olive McDermott, the Western Union telegraph operators who had transmitted the bogus messages from Denver to New York.

Customers of the bank who were called to testify included George Young, a prominent ranch and sheep owner; Clyde Porter, one of Waggoner's trusted friends; C.R. Blanchard; Robert Valiant; R.O. Dillon; Dr. E.H. Taylor; and John C. Anderson. The latter two, the prosecution would argue, had been given dummy positions in two cattle and land companies that Waggoner had set up and manipulated for personal gain. Harry Miller, a shareholder of the bank, longtime local barber, and perhaps Waggoner's closest personal friend, was also called as a witness, not because the authorities had anything against him, Kleid and Tuttle had explained to Judge Coleman, but because they wanted to find out whether or not Waggoner had been "confidential" under the soothing influence of shaving lather.

Waggoner's wife, Mary, was in attendance, but not by subpoena. Tuttle had hired Leonard De Lue of De Lue Secret Service to find traces of a rumored five thousand dollar certified draft sent by Waggoner to his wife, but De Lue had been unsuccessful in the attempt. As a result, the U.S. District Attorney decided against putting Mary Waggoner on the stand, feeling that she would elicit only empathy from the judge. On the other hand, he had definitely wanted Waggoner, Jr., as a witness — the young man's bitterness, shame, and anger were that palpable.

One after the other the witnesses took the stand and Crump artfully, subtly, coaxed from them testimonials of Waggoner's long, steady captaincy at the helm of the bank, of his unwavering community spirit, and his dedication to his wife and child. Over and over, Crump was able to get the witnesses to depict Waggoner, in their own words, as a long-suffering and unselfish servant of the welfare of Telluride and its citizenry. Then, just as artfully but with no attempt at subtlety, Tuttle turned the testimonies away from praise and tributes, deliberately, precisely, like a sculptor working in marble, chipping away at the façade of Waggoner's persona to display an underlying identity that had not before been revealed. Much of the evidence that he used came from information subpoenaed from Grant McFerson's examination team. The witnesses he called to the stand he had culled knowledgably, based on that information.

The damning accounts that the witnesses disgorged were not given up with zeal. No one from Telluride, it seemed, wanted Buck Waggoner to pay an undue price for his acts. Unlike Tuttle, they could not look at the facts and draw from them an unwavering conclusion of what type of man Waggoner was or how willful were his crimes. This was not just a case for them, a legal contest to be won or lost, or a matter of marshalling words and accounts together to make the best, most convincing story — the one to which the judge would give the most weight. There was far more to it than that for them. Considering facts was one thing, but considering a man they knew and liked and respected — a man like them, someone who was part of the very fabric of their lives — was something altogether different: something far less definite and far more difficult. They could not, however, withhold evidence. They were under oath, most of them for the first time in their lives. They were simple people caught as if in an avalanche by events and proceedings that had momentum and power that they could not refute or avoid.

Alta could plainly see the pain in their expressions. They had not come on their own to be part of their friend's, their banker's, prosecution. They had come by order of the law, and regardless of what the prosecution coaxed, wrested, or simply induced from them, Alta doubted there was a single soul among them all who would not have personally pardoned Waggoner, or who would have felt justice had been miscarried if the judge were to pardon him.

George Young had been the first witness. He testified that he had given Waggoner a note for twenty-five hundred dollars, for which he received credit. Later on, Young claimed, Waggoner had told him that the bank wanted to rediscount the note, include it as part of a package of notes to be used as collateral for a loan to the Bank of Telluride from one of its correspondent banks. Waggoner asked him to sign a new note with a longer maturity that would be more satisfactory to the correspondent bank; the note would then be less likely to be paid off, and so no substitution of other collateral during the term of the Telluride bank's borrowing would be required. Having confidence in the bank's head, Young signed the new note, only to learn from McFerson's examination of the bank that five thousand dollars was recorded as outstanding against him, instead of just half of that, which is what he had actually received.

Clyde Porter, so trusting that he never kept account of the number of notes he signed nor the amount of his indebtedness, submitted under Tuttle's questioning that Waggoner offered to finance him in the sheep business but, before doing so, extracted a written agreement from him. Under this arrangement, Porter agreed to give Waggoner a half-interest in his real estate and sheep in consideration that Waggoner would, without cost to himself, finance Porter out of his bank's funds.

C.R. Blanchard told a similar story under examination. He testified that Waggoner had given him, without consideration, lands standing in the name of the bank and then loaned him money from the bank in consideration that Blanchard would deed to Waggoner an undivided half-interest in the land and the sheep grown on it.

Robert Valiant, an old-time cow man who had gone broke in the slump of 1919 and 1920, revealed that though he was entirely without credit, Waggoner approached him and delegated him to purchase cattle, the money for which was to be advanced by the bank. Valiant did so for several years, and always when he drew his checks, the bank furnished the funds. As with Blanchard and Porter, Waggoner, according to Valiant, extracted an agreement to be a silent partner in Valiant's business and to receive a full half-share of profit from sale of the land and cattle. The venture, Valiant conceded, was not ultimately a profitable one.

Two witnesses, Dr. E.H. Taylor and John C. Anderson, claimed that through misrepresentation by Waggoner, they had been duped into becoming involved in land and cattle enterprises that existed only on paper, but for which they were induced to sign fraudulent notes to the tune of some thirty thousand dollars.

In questioning Grant McFerson, Tuttle was able to reveal to the court that the estate of Henry Baisch, a well-known and trusted friend of Waggoner's, had still not been settled eight years after the pharmacist's murder. Money and assets of the estate, McFerson conceded, had disappeared, with notes of Clyde Porter, Robert Valiant, and others having been substituted, even though none of the alleged makers of the notes could recall ever signing a debt instrument to Baisch, either personally before his death or to his estate afterwards.

Perhaps the most compelling testimony came from Waggoner's personal assistant, Miss Alice Lingren. As with the other witnesses, Samuel Crump was successful in getting Miss Lingren to extol the virtues of her boss's kindness, sobriety, devotion to his business, his town, and his family and friends. Then, with the ease and speed of an angler gutting a fish, Tuttle extracted from her confessions of forging notes at Waggoner's direction. The first instance involved a mortgage note from Leslie Doss. When Doss became unable to repay the note and, as agreed, deeded his land to the bank to satisfy his obligation, Judge Hoy, county judge and local counsel for the bank, delivered to Doss and cancelled all the notes that he had ever executed to the bank. Subsequently, Waggoner had his assistant forge Doss's name on a note for approximately fifteen thousand dollars. Likewise, Miss Lingren, still trusting her employer, forged the name of R.O. Dillon, who had closed his account with the bank several years before, on a note in the amount of twelve thousand dollars. She later signed notes for Waggoner aggregating some fifteen thousand dollars with the name of Dr. Taylor on behalf of the Shenandoah Land and Cattle Company. All of these bogus notes were claimed as assets by the bank, and many of them were used as security for loans to the Bank of Telluride from banks in Denver and New York.

"I had no idea," sobbed the witness, "I had no idea that what I was doing was wrong. I didn't know very much about banking, and Mr. Waggoner made it seem as if what he was asking me to do was normal practice. I was a new girl, and he had been president for such a long time, I never even questioned what I was asked to do."

Alta and Nick both took copious notes during the testimonies. Alta found herself squeezing Nick's arm involuntarily when Tuttle provoked particularly damning evidence from her reticent neighbors and friends. Each time she did, he patted her hand lightly or pressed it with his own.

※ ※ ※

Midday came and went, a half-hour break for lunch was taken, and the afternoon bore on with further testimony. The light coming in through the tall, streaked window had changed from wan to a febrile yellow. Waggoner continued to watch the pigeons and had come to realize that it was not a random set of arrivals and departures, not a changing cast of birds. It was one small flock, possibly a family, and there was a deliberate, though not always predictable, pattern to their comings and goings. Waggoner wondered what it would take to disrupt that pattern. What predators, he wondered, did the pigeons have, apart from automobiles and buses? Were there hawks in the city?

Probably not, at least not enough of them to represent a serious threat. Foxes, he imagined, lived in the city. Foxes were just about everywhere. And feral cats, he was sure, lived in the city's parks and back alleys. Probably, though, he reasoned, age was the primary hunter of pigeons in the city, along with disease, disease carried invisibly into the New York port from all around the world. Someone had once told him that pigeons were notorious carriers of germs and sickness. Who had it been? Was it Wells? Yes, it had been. Wells had said that pigeons were his least favorite animals. He called them winged vermin or feathered rats, or some such thing.

Waggoner closed his eyes and saw Bulkeley Wells as clearly as if he were standing in front of him. He pictured him dressed as he almost always was — unless he was wearing his absurd military costume as head of the Citizens' Alliance — in a spotlessly clean and expensively tailored suit made by Italians from fabric that came from China or somewhere equally impossible. Apart from the one his uncle had paid for and that Mary Reade had helped him to choose shortly after his arrival in Telluride, Waggoner had never owned a custom-made suit in his life. Indeed, he was often inclined to jackets and pants that didn't even match and that had been darned in a dozen places. How very different they had been, Wells and he: one tall, the other short; one handsome, the other not; one refined, cultured, arrogant, rich; the other plain, simple, modest. It was always quite astounding to him that he and Wells could have become such friends in the early days. But they had. However improbably, they certainly had. The Citizens' Alliance had stuck in Waggoner's craw, to be sure; all the injustice of it, all the cruel unfairness —all the pompous military righteousness. No, he hadn't held with that at all. But he had forgiven Wells for the part he played, just as he always forgave him every transgression.

"You know what I hate, Charles?" Wells had once asked him entirely out of the blue. "I hate pigeons. I deplore the dirty things."

Wells had just come back from a week-long affair at the Biltmore in Colorado Springs. It had to do with Harvard or the Livermores or the Whitneys, or some high and mighty group or another. Waggoner could no longer recall. He himself had never been invited to any gala events in Colorado Springs, where it was said that the worst possible social affliction was to be considered boring.

It was then that Wells had described the birds as vermin or rats. "That's one of the things I love most about Telluride," he declared. "No fucking pigeons."

He had been drinking a bit. They were headed for the National Club, a gambling hall presided over by Morris "Big Mike" Lehman. It was one of Wells' favorite spots, because it attracted a particularly rakish crowd, both men and women. For all his elegance and sophistication, Wells had a decided penchant for the wrong side of the street. And it never cost him anything socially — not in the early days, anyway. It was a man's town then, and Wells was at the top of the heap.

At the National Club, as with most of Telluride's drinking and gambling establishments, there were few strictures governing patrons' behavior. One habitual denizen kept his pet goat by his side whenever he gambled, stroking its long whiskers for luck. In the basement, at the back of the building, was a small room fitted with low backless couches, its floor covered by richly colored carpets, its walls hung with oriental tapestries. Here, Charley Fong Ding, laundryman for the girls on Pacific Street, would stick a small, rubbery, brown ball of opium in a pipe and patiently wait until his customer was ready, Charley's rheumy eyes just slits in his yellow creased face. Then deftly, carefully, as solicitous as a Finn or a Swede lighting dynamite, he would light the pipe, putting the flame of his match into the bowl, then taking it out, probing at the opium with the matchstick, turning the ball delicately, so that it would soon glow fully and evenly like a miniature sun poised to set.

Waggoner had once tried Charley's pipe, at Wells' insistence, of course. He didn't know which was worse, the violent physical illness that beset him, or the uncontrollable and bizarre mutations of his thoughts. The combination of the two was more than enough to ensure he would never try it again. Wells, on the other hand, suffered neither sickness nor anxiety, and, though he did not often allow himself to be seen descending the basement stairs of the National, he was, during certain periods at least, one of Charley Fong Ding's most regular customers. Then, just as he was courting addiction, he would quit the stuff for months at a time.

Charley Fong Ding, as Waggoner had heard the story, had come from Shanghai as the servant of a beautiful Chinese woman (some said she was Charley's niece), who was the concubine of a Scottish engineer. They arrived in Telluride in the '80s — the engineer, his wife and child, and the two Chinese. The engineer purchased two adjoining lots in town and built a house on each. One house was traditional Victorian, the other built in the style of Chinese houses. The Chinese woman was rarely seen, but those who glimpsed her described a stunning beauty with luxuriant and intricately arranged hair the color of jet, piled high on her head and held in place by decorative jade combs and pins. Her skin was said to be the color of pale moonlight.

Within a year of completing the houses, the engineer was killed when an elevator cable snapped, and the cage in which he was riding with three others plunged a thousand feet down a mine shaft. Following his funeral and burial at the Lone Tree, his wife packed up her household and emigrated back to Scotland, leaving Charley Fong Ding and the Chinese woman behind. Before she left, the engineer's wife had the two turned out of their oriental house, and then she had the house torn down and the lot sold. The Chinese woman was taken in by Diamond Tooth Leona, a bluff but good-hearted madam. Leona's new charge was highly prized by the wealthier johns for, in addition to great beauty, she possessed a refinement of manners that was more than rare. Whether from a broken heart or simply shame, she turned to the opium that Charley was able to supply. She became a chronic addict. In less than a year, she died of consumption, having never lost, even into her last days, her luminous beauty.

After her death, Charley worked for several different bawdy houses on the south side of town, doing laundry and running errands. He kept an opium pipe in each and, for a fee, he would prepare them for customers and their consorts. Bulkeley Wells was a favored customer at all the houses, though his clear personal favorite was the Pick 'n' Gad. It was owned by Laura LaRue, a brainy and handsome woman who had retreated to society's demimonde after a knifeman had mapped her face with a jagged meridian from scalp to jaw. LaRue was one of the only women in Telluride who could match Wells in charm and savoir-faire. She called her establishment a *maison de joie*, and it had its own highly accomplished cook, a full cherry bar, and a Negro woman who played the piano and who had, so Laura LaRue said, a double major in music from a Massachusetts conservatory. Waggoner could easily believe it. Never before or since had he heard anyone play an instrument with such delicacy or certainty or with such stirring flourishes.

Waggoner opened his eyes. The pigeons were now all together on the window ledge, come home to roost, he thought, at the end of the day.

※ ※ ※

The bailiff called Harry Miller to take the stand. Waggoner felt a slight quickening of his pulse. Miller would be the last witness before he himself was called. How odd, he thought, that he should muse on Bulkeley Wells just prior to Miller's testimony. Miller had, over the years, been his other closest friend. Like him, Miller was in most ways the complete opposite of Wells. He was of humble origins and a self-made man, never dependent on anyone for favor or fortune. He plied his trade as a barber from sunup to sundown, six days a week, every week of the year, with just one week off during fishing season. His clientele was mostly miners, and he charged them a uniform twenty-five cents for a haircut and fifty-cents for a shave. If a rich man came in for a cut, or brought in his son, Miller charged him a dollar, two for a shave. Over time, Miller earned and saved a quite adequate fortune and invested significantly in stock of the Bank of Telluride. He also supplemented his wealth with winnings at the card table and at roulette. He was an avid gambler, and in this, he and Wells were able to establish a mutuality of spirit. In most everything else, they were at constant odds. Funny, Waggoner thought, that Miller, who had come to Telluride with no money of his own and no backing, had made a clear success of himself, while Wells, who had arrived with fortunes at his disposal, was now barely managing. Or so he had heard. Since Wells had deserted his wife and four children and departed town with a curvaceous, platinum blonde who was half his age, Waggoner had had no further contact with his old friend. Word was, though, that he had married the blonde and that he was struggling badly financially, all his prior backers having cut him off.

As Harry Miller took the stand, Waggoner took off his small glasses, shut his eyes again, and pinched his nose at the top of its bridge. He sighed, feeling as if his spirit was fleeing him. He was going down, he knew. He was bound for the "Big House," as his miner friends referred to jail. Even if Miller lauded him with every possible tribute and compliment, it would be a matter of "too little, too late," Waggoner knew. The damage was done, the die cast.

As if she could read the banker's thoughts, Alta found herself concurring increasingly with his assessment as the witnesses came and went. No matter how adroitly the banker's attorney coaxed them into accolades of his client's character and commitment to his community, the federal attorney turned that testimony on its head time and again. And, whereas the defense attorney tended toward generality and rather sweeping overview, the prosecutor was a stickler for hard facts and carefully focused questions. By the time Harry Miller took the witness stand, the case for Waggoner seemed decidedly weak. From witnesses whom Alta trusted implicitly came allegation after allegation of skull-duggery by the bank president. Certainly abundant evidence had been supplied that Waggoner was a good man, a kind man, and an upstanding civic citizen, but those testimonials provided scant but-tressing against charges from his own customers, and even his per-sonal assistant, of fraudulent activity. And yet, however convincing the case against him was becoming, the question still remained in Alta's mind: Why? Why had he done all these things he was accused of? Why had he taken such risks: risk of exposure, risk of opprobrium, risk of arrest and jail and ruin?

Nick Alexander had the same question, and he jotted it on Alta's pad in large script: WHY?

CHAPTER EIGHTEEN

Harry Miller made a deliberate detour on his way to the witness stand so that he could pass closely enough to Waggoner to be able to lightly squeeze his friend's shoulder. The banker made no movement in response.

Unlike his fellow townspeople, Miller seemed as relaxed on the stand as if he was sitting in one of the big swivel chairs in his shop on Colorado Avenue, where Alta regularly saw him holding court to his clients. From the answers that he gave to the lawyers, and the manner of them, it was plain that he had no intention of saying anything about Waggoner that could be perceived in a bad light. This made for light work of the defense lawyer's job, but for the prosecution, it posed a challenge. The young district attorney seemed delighted to accept it.

"Tell me, Mr. Miller," he probed, raising his spectacles above his eyes, making a show of studying his notes. "What is the nature of your relationship with the defendant? Is he a person with whom you would consider yourself very well acquainted?"

Miller answered, "You cut a man's hair for almost twenty years, you get to know him pretty well. Play cards with him, bank with him, go to church with him — there comes a point where there's probably not much you don't know about him."

The district attorney seemed to have been provided just the opening he wanted. "I see. Then am I to be given to understand, Mr. Miller, that despite your complete and, dare I say, deep acquaintance with the defendant, you had no idea whatsoever of his stratagem to defraud the Denver and New York banks?"

"You can understand what you like, sir. Only thing I know is that Buck Waggoner is an honest man. Whatever he did or didn't do with those banks, I'm sure he had just cause."

"And how would you define a 'just cause?'"

Miller tightened his lips, taking a slow breath through his nose. "I would define a just cause," he answered, speaking carefully and looking directly at the district attorney, "as one where the ends justify the means. In this case, whatever Buck did to get money back to the folks in Telluride that would have otherwise lost it, was a just cause. The New York banks and the Denver banks were only too happy to take money out of Telluride for many years. I'd hate to think of the kind of profits they made on our town and its mines. When times were good, they took their interest and their fees and smiled like brides on honeymoon. Then, when things toughened, they walked out of the marriage at the first chance they got, taking every penny they could find, not caring a fig whether the town lived or died. When the town really needed them, the big banks were as scarce in our neck of the woods as jackalopes."

A titter arose from the Telluridians in the room. Nick looked at Alta, his eyebrows raised. The DA asked the question for him.

"Jackalopes?"

"Yessir. That's a cross between a rabbit and an antelope."

It took a long moment for the lawyer to realize the joke. When he did, he smiled mirthlessly, then waited for the judge's gavel to silence an outburst of laughter.

"Have you anything further?" he posed.

"Yes, I do," Miller responded. "Buck Waggoner, who is not and never was a fair-weather banker, *did* care whether our town survived. He cared with all his heart and soul. Turnabout is fair play in my book, sir. And that's what I consider Buck gave those banks — fair play. And he did it for folks that could not have done it for themselves. That, to me, is a just cause, sir, no matter what the law may have to say about it."

Enthusiastic applause sounded from several sections of the courtroom, and the judge's gavel again struck repeatedly.

The prosecutor conferred with his associates before resuming his questioning. While he did, Alta studied Harry Miller. As long as she had known him, as many times as she had passed him on the street and seen him in his shop or in Perino's or Van Atta's stores, she had never paid very close attention to his appearance. She had never really remarked his height, which seemed pronounced now by the large witness chair he sat in and that had made so many of the other witnesses seem so small to her. Miller was well over six feet and seemed, because of his ranginess, his wide shoulders, big hands and feet, and long arms, even taller. Though speckled liberally with gray, his hair was still full and thick and mostly black. His eyes were deep set and dark, and his nose broke the plane of his face like a rock outcropping on a cliff wall. He was a handsome man, Alta decided, with clean, strong features that gave his face an uncomplicated quality. It was an honest face.

"Mr. Miller," said Tuttle, returning to the witness. "You say that you were in the habit of playing cards with Mr. Waggoner. What type of games did you play? Were these just friendly games, or more of a wagering variety?"

"Oh, we wager, sir. Absolutely. But that doesn't mean they aren't friendly. Mostly we play poker of one kind or another, sometimes blackjack, fan-tan, seven-and-a-half. And faro, of course."

"I see. Would you be able to characterize for the court what type of player Mr. Waggoner was? Was he modest in his wagers, for example? Did he ever welsh on a bet?"

"Buck's a savvy card player. He could have a straight flush or a pair of deuces, and you'd never know which. As far as placing a bet and upping the ante, he's not afraid of either. But he never bet more than he could afford to lose, and he never went into anyone's debt."

"Would you say that he won more often than lost?"

"I can't say I kept track. We've been playing cards for many years. Given that kind of time, winning and losing tend to even themselves out."

"What type of stakes did you typically play for, Mr. Miller? On a good night, let's say, how much could you hope to take home over and above what you came with?"

"If I left with what I came with, that was a pretty good night. A winning night might see me five hundred dollars better off than when I started. Sometimes more."

"Did you ever lose that much in a night?"

Miller laughed. "I've been known to have a streak of cold hands, yes."

"And Mr. Waggoner?"

"The same."

"But he never had any problem covering his losses?"

"No sir, none."

"Have there been times over the years when players did encounter difficulties, Mr. Miller? Times when they couldn't cover their losses?"

"Of course. More than a few."

"And was it generally known whether a player was on the financial edge, as it were?"

Miller thought for a moment. "Sometimes yes, sometimes no. Depends on the person, really, and how freely he spoke of his affairs."

"Did Mr. Waggoner ever speak of his affairs?"

"No, sir."

"Were you personally aware of his financial condition?"

"Well, not fully, no. As a stockholder in the bank, I knew what he was being paid."

"But you didn't know more than that? You had no idea, for instance, of the extent of his obligations or the success or failure of his personal investments?"

Miller shook his head. "No, sir. None. He has a fine house, a nice car, one of the best jobs, maybe the best job, in town. He's not a drinker or a carouser, doesn't own a stable full of racehorses. I've never had any reason to think that his financial condition was anything but sound."

"But you don't actually know, were never told one way or the other by Mr. Waggoner?"

"No."

"How many times a week, on average, did Mr. Waggoner gamble at cards?"

"Maybe four or five times."

"Four or five times a week, every week, for what? Can we say fifteen years? Perhaps more?"

"Oh, I don't know exactly. Seems to me we started playing regularly back in the days when Bulkeley Wells was made manager of the Smuggler-Union Mine, so that's more like twenty-five years ago. But we didn't play so often back then. Maybe just once or twice a week."

"In any case," offered Tuttle, "many games over many years. And if a five hundred dollar night was not unheard of, winning or losing, then it could be safe to conjecture that a player may have lost a considerable amount over that period, especially if the wins and losses did not quite 'even out,' as you put it. Even at a much lower number, say an average loss of just fifty or seventy-five dollars, an amount not terribly conspicuous, a player could have descended into financial difficulties quite easily and deeply."

"It's possible," conceded Miller, "but as I said, in Buck's case, he never had a problem covering his losses, so it wouldn't seem to me that he suffered too much financial hardship."

"Which brings me to my point precisely," responded the attorney, now speaking directly to the judge. "A man in Mr. Waggoner's position, as president of the Bank of Telluride, would have been able to easily access and appropriate funds that were not his own and then use those funds to cover his debts. Which is, in fact, exactly what appears to have transpired. I believe Mr. Waggoner, overly devoted to the thrill of gambling, managed to place himself in quite dire economic straits. To solve his problems, I believe he liberated sizable amounts of cash and securities from his bank. And then, in an effort to cover evidence of his defalcation, he replaced the bank's missing assets with securities that he took from safe deposit boxes of certain of his customers, as well as with spurious notes drawn on estates entrusted to his fiduciary care. I submit that some of the estates he looted were those of widows and orphans. I believe he indulged himself in this pattern of deception and fraud for many years, and that he was motivated to arrange the half-million dollar swindle of the New York banks more by fear of being exposed by a pending bank examination than by any altruistic concern for his depositors."

The courtroom was silent. Alta put her hand on Alexander's knee and squeezed it. Her eyes, as were everyone else's, were on the banker as he sat, impassive, staring out the window.

"Bingo," whispered Alexander, letting his hand rest on top of hers.

※ ※ ※

When his name was called by the bailiff, Waggoner made no move to respond. He sat as still as he had all day, as apparently unaware of his whereabouts or the weight of the proceedings against him as a man in a coma. For the first time, the courtroom was in complete silence.

"Charles Delos Waggoner," the bailiff called out again. "Please take the stand."

The banker moved not a muscle. Samuel Crump and Elwood Rabenald leaned toward him from either side and whispered urgently to him. Slowly the banker stood at last and approached the witness stand. He turned, and for the first time the press and gallery could see his face. His expression was wan, tired, drawn. His eyes, though looking out at the assembly before him, appeared unseeing.

The bailiff presented the Bible to him and asked him to raise his right hand. Waggoner refused. The bailiff repeated his demand and was refused again. Judge Coleman ordered the attorneys to approach the bench. The hushed tones of their conference were indistinguishable to the rest of the courtroom, from whom a buzz of chatter now arose to replace the prior silence. The judge banged his gavel sharply and the buzz subsided.

"The attorneys for the defense have been informed that their client may be held in contempt of court for refusing to take an oath of honesty. The attorneys for the prosecution have requested that proceedings continue and the defense has agreed. Mr. Waggoner, please be seated."

"I prefer to stand," Waggoner replied.

The judge closed his eyes as if unable to choose his next words. "As you like, sir. You may remain standing."

Mary Waggoner felt as if her heart would break. Her husband looked like a man without a friend in the world. His thin lips seemed as if they had never, could never again curve into the sweet, shy smile she knew so well. Mary knew that what her husband had done was wrong, terribly wrong. At the same time, she knew his heart was good. He had never been anything but a kind and generous man. He had been ready for as long as she had known him to help whoever he could, however he could. His life had been devoted to her, to his son, and to their town. However much he may have erred in judgment, whatever he had done that he shouldn't have, he was still a good man, and one who deserved none of the aspersion cast on him by the federal attorney. Who were these people, she thought, to pass judgment on him? What did they know of real trials, of the trials of a town facing its extinction? Of friends pushed to the brink of ruin, of good, hard-working people faced with losing all they had ever striven for? Why, she wondered, were the New York and the Denver banks not on trial for having no other interest in her husband, his bank, or in Telluride than their chance for profit?

Beside her, her son felt none of her compassion. The hatred that had formed in his heart hardened, his shame deepened. He had not proved a very effective witness when he had taken the stand. Under questioning, he had been able to reveal only negligible knowledge of the bank's condition or of its policies and procedures. He had stepped down from the stand feeling like a buffoon, an unimportant pawn, guilty of playing no more than a completely meaningless role at the bank; guilty of dishonor and betrayal of trust by dint of his blood, his name.

In answering the questions posed to him by the lawyers, Waggoner spoke softly and low, occasioning the press and spectators to lean forward, cup their ears, and refrain from making the least noise. As he had since his arrest, Waggoner repeated his claim that his sole intention and ambition had been to save the bank's depositors. He defended what he had done strictly in those terms and denied that he had done anything ever to improperly enrich himself or to put his customers in jeopardy.

He spoke of the way of life in Telluride, the town's smallness and sense of community. He explained that his customers — those that he so ardently wanted to help, to safeguard — were, in most instances, friends of many years. They were people, he stated, whom he saw every week, if not every day. He described the role of a bank in such a community as vitally important, its ability to make loans and take in deposits as critical to the town's well-being as rainfall and sunshine and the rule of law as governed by elected officials.

"My bank, the Bank of Telluride," he stated without braggadocio, "is the lifeblood of my town. With it, life is sustained. Without it, there is no life. If I resorted to irregularities, and I make no pretense that I did not, it was a matter of exigency. I saw no other means to cover the bank's deteriorating capital position, no other way to keep it afloat."

"Mr. Waggoner," pressed the district attorney, who made no effort to conceal in his voice the contempt with which he listened to the banker's justifications, "did you or did you not sustain losses from gambling that served to place you in a difficult personal financial position?"

"I did," Waggoner admitted.

"And how did you address that difficulty?"

"I borrowed money."

"As a banker, Mr. Waggoner, you understand better than most that borrowing money implies its future repayment. Were you able to repay the money you borrowed?"

"I have never been seriously delinquent on repayment of any debt."

"And what was the source of your payments?"

"In some cases, I liquidated investments. I used my earnings from the bank. In some cases, I took out additional loans."

"Did you ever 'borrow' money from your own bank?"

"No."

"Were the investments that you 'liquidated' fair and legitimate ones, ones that you were unable to manipulate by your position as president of the Bank of Telluride?"

"Yes."

"I see," said Tuttle, making a show of removing his glasses and pinching the bridge of his sharp nose. "And yet, Mr. Waggoner, we have heard repeated testimony today from witnesses, witnesses culled from among your own customers, that indicates quite clearly that you defrauded them and that you personally profited at their expense. They have told of sham investments and bogus notes, of missing securities, forgery, of nonexistent loans carried on the bank's books as good assets. It is known, irrefutably, that you paid back a personal note of indebtedness for seventy thousand dollars with part of the funds that you illegally obtained from the New York banks. How do you account for all of that? How, in good conscience, can you tell us that you did nothing wrong in the face of your personal financial difficulty, that your investments were all legitimate, that your 'loans' were honestly obtained and honestly repaid?"

"My conscience, sir," answered Waggoner, almost in a whisper, "is perfectly clear. It was not my debt that motivated me to any of the actions you describe. My troubles and the bank's troubles, the town's troubles, are separate and distinct, and I dealt with them as such. Failure of the Bank of Telluride was a prospect that I could not countenance. I would not allow it. It would have been the death knell for my town and my community. All that was needed was time. With time, with patience, things would have turned around. The people of Telluride are resourceful. And they can bear up under hardship as well as any people in the world. One way or another, I knew that they could get through our tough patch and surmount their difficulties. But they couldn't do it immediately, and they couldn't do it on their own. They needed time, and they needed the bank's help. And those, sir, are what all my efforts were intended to provide."

"Then, doubling the amount of debt claimed by the bank to be outstanding from a borrower and ransacking an unsettled estate of its assets and replacing them with spurious ones were simply methods of yours to help the borrower and the beneficiaries of the estate. Is that it?"

Waggoner nodded. "It is."

"And repaying a large personal note with money stolen in the name of the Bank of Telluride is simply part of keeping the bank alive, of helping its community to survive?"

Waggoner nodded again. "It was purely due to the difficult times of the town and the bank that I originally borrowed the money that I repaid. That money went to replenishing the bank's coffers as deposits dried up and loans went delinquent. Everything I did, everything that you look at with suspicion and scorn, I did not for myself but for my bank and my community. I am not a saint, sir. But neither am I the sinner you make me out to be. Given the chance, I would rob the New York banks again. Given the chance, I would manipulate and rig things as best I could and in any way that I could to save my bank and my town from failure. If that is wrong, then I am happy not to be right. If that is a crime, then I am happy not to be innocent of it."

Waggoner turned his eyes to the judge, and then back to the district attorney before speaking again. "I have nothing further to say. Whatever questions you still may have, I will not answer them. The court may well hold me in contempt. What is that to me? It cannot compare to the contempt in which I hold a system where the rich and powerful make mockery of justice every day. Where men guilty of far worse crimes than mine are lauded as leaders of their communities and even of this country. Walk down Wall Street any day, sir, and you will be rubbing well-dressed shoulders with men who could not care less about a widow or an orphan or anything but profit. You talk of legitimate investments, and yet every day, more millions of dollars are invested on Wall Street in scams and hoaxes than you could possibly guess. I am not a rich man. I have not stolen money from anyone to become richer. I could as easily have taken the half-million dollars for myself and hidden somewhere for the rest of my days, where no one would have found me. But I didn't. It was not my intent. My intent was to get money back to people who would otherwise not get it back. That was all. And however you choose to twist the meaning of what I did, the simple fact remains that I did it for others, not for myself."

With that, Waggoner stepped down and returned to his seat. No one tried to stop him. After a pause of quiet, the courtroom resounded with loud applause that the judge's gavel was powerless to quell.

CHAPTER NINETEEN

Alta and Nick did not agree in their opinions of Waggoner's testimony. The difference in their perspectives would be evident in the articles that they each wrote. Nick's, of course, would reach a far greater readership, but Alta's was read not only by everyone in San Miguel County and surrounds, but by small-town readers throughout the West. Her story was picked up by a dozen different newspaper publishers, and her trip expenses were more than covered by the fees they paid. Best of all, one of the publishers was interested in Alta's preliminary work on Telluride's history.

"So," chided Nick, "looks as if you may beat me to the ranks of real writers, mystery or otherwise."

Alta smiled and shook her head. Talk was cheap, she knew. She would not allow herself to become excited about the possibilities of a book until she had something concrete to go by.

"Whenever you do reach the ranks," she answered him, her eyes mischievous, "I'm sure you'll do well. Fiction seems to come naturally to you."

Alta had stayed in New York for a number of days after the trial in order to complete her article. She and Nick had dined together each night. Their argument over Waggoner was ongoing. Nick refused to be drawn in by the bait she had just thrown him. He smiled and shrugged instead. They were walking in Central Park after enjoying high tea at Alta's hotel. It was Sunday afternoon. Alta would be leaving the next day to return to Telluride. As much as she missed home, she was not looking forward to leaving.

They had been in the park for an hour, strolling, people watching, talking. It had been a mild afternoon that was now tailing off into dusk. The leaves on the trees and those that had blown off wore the colors of fall. The air, warmed by unbroken sunshine all day, was now tinged by a chill. Alta liked the crisp feel of the air, the rich scent of the changing leaves. She slipped her arm into Nick's and he pressed it against his body.

They had already kissed, twice, in parting at night. Alta had written in her diary that the first kiss was how she imagined the touch of a fairy-tale wand might be. It had been shocking, but deliciously so. It had sent an electric thrill through her while, at the same time, she had become enveloped by a soft cloud of timelessness that transported her from the moment and from every thought. The second kiss was better than the first.

Over their dinners and walks, Alta had described Telluride for Nick. She described the light of morning that made the highest peaks shine as if they were incandescent and the light of the afternoon that burnished them with a golden-pink glow. She shared with him the magic of riding horseback through high alpine meadows rimmed by aspens, whose leaves were like water in their tremulous sensitivity to the merest breeze; of the thrill of coming upon a herd of elk while riding, and galloping in the midst of them, their tawny hides turned cinnamon by the sun, their pungent smell and the stampeding sound of them as they ran. She told him of the snow, how it came down so hard and fast that you couldn't see anything but its infinite flakes and how, blue-white and sparkling with the colors of a rainbow, it settled after storms in impossibly smooth contours that looked like a woman's naked curves.

"We ski and toboggan in the winter," she told him. "Sometimes we go too fast and hit a bump that sends us sailing. We crash with some frequency."

She pictured for him picnics in summer along the banks of the river or beside waterfalls, of bathing in limpid, icy pools amid moss-cushioned rocks, and of climbing high into basins ribboned by streams and wrapped in wildflowers. She told him of the hummingbirds that darted and hovered, and that sometimes, if you had on bright clothing, came so close that you could feel the air beaten by their tireless, translucent wings.

Nick told her that he wanted to come and see it all for himself, wanted to come to see her there.

They stood in the park at the edge of a lake and watched geese move across its darkening water as if some invisible force propelled them, their paddling webbed feet hidden from view.

Nick turned Alta to face him and moved his hands to press her to him. Her lips parted as if they were in control of her rather than the other way round. Nick kissed her for the third time, and she offered him no resistance.

There were certainly points of agreement between what Alta wrote of the grand jury trial and what Nick wrote. But, on the point of his gambling, a point on which Tuttle drummed again and again and on which Waggoner was as repeatedly dismissive, the coverage by Alta and Nick diverged. Nick, convinced that a deeper and darker motivation than altruism was at the root of Waggoner's actions, made the banker's habitual gambling a centerpiece of his article. Alta gave it scarce mention.

"There is simply no proof," she had argued with Alexander, her eyes just moments before soft and smiling, now penetrating his with firm resolve. "There is no proof at all that he covered gambling losses with the bank's money."

"Perhaps not proof in any absolute sense," countered Alexander, "but there's enough circumstantial evidence to sink a ship. Exhibit A: a bank president who is an inveterate gambler; Exhibit B: a bank with disappearing funds, fraudulent notes, forged obligations. A plus B equals C, the way I look at it, and C stands for crooked."

Alta refused to see it that way or to write it. It wasn't that she was naïve. She knew well enough that gambling could take over a person's life as easily as alcohol or laudanum. The fact was, however, she did not believe that Buck Waggoner would ever allow his life, so ordered in other respects, to unravel so significantly. She did not believe that he would pawn the bank that he had spent his adult life managing and caring for, for the sake of cards. Nor did she accept that he would risk all that he had — his reputation, his relationships with friends and family, his freedom — to cover his tracks. He could have as easily, more easily in fact, simply disappeared and suffered little of the infamy and contumely that was currently his due. He had put himself at stake for half a million dollars. It was a sum that she could not bring herself to believe had any real relation to a personal financial plight. And it struck her as outlandish to conceive that he would arrange such a large and elaborate swindle simply to obfuscate his own private misdeeds.

In a way, she thought, although she didn't say so, Nick's was an easier angle to report. It was more black and white, more simplistic. By his angle, Waggoner was depicted as a bad man who was caught doing bad things. There was purity to the angle, a sharpness unadulterated by the dulling effect of contravening details. It was a line that readers could easily follow, assimilate, understand. The moral equation was straightforward. Alta knew that newspaper readers, by and large, didn't care to have their faculties tested. They didn't want to have to weigh facts, make educated and sometimes difficult associations or connections, to be pushed to "ratiocination," as Dad Painter might have put it. People read newspapers, she knew, to be told what was what. They read newspapers to get facts that they could register, accept, and either remember or forget. For newspaper readers, Nick's story would fit all the necessary criteria. When they read what he wrote — that C.D. Waggoner had a gambling problem, one that may have caused him to lose a great deal of money, losses that may have been made up by stealing from his own bank — it would fit their natural need for a closed circle of cause and effect. Knowing their own human natures, they would also readily identify with the banker succumbing to temptation. They would not approve or excuse him, necessarily, but they would, personally and easily, accept the possibility.

Alta's premise, based on Waggoner's testimony, was that he had done bad things in the service of a greater and overarching good. It was his bank he was trying to save, and his customers, not himself. The forgeries, the irregularities, and the fraud that he had committed were desperate measures born of desperate times, and they were capped by a final attempt, more desperate than any that preceded it, one with severest consequences, to put things to right for the people that he had so long served. Alta refused not to believe that. She refused because of the person she had always known Buck Waggoner to be; she refused because of what she had seen in his eyes the night he drove his Studebaker out of town. She had seen the same look in his eyes, one not of guilt or remorse but simply sadness, as he testified at his trial. Alta did not subscribe wholeheartedly to women's intuition: She knew too many women who seemed to have none. In this case, however, she had a powerful conviction emanating from a part of herself for which she knew no other name.

There was something else, too. As she had explained to Dad Painter, regardless of what was written by others — whether for or against Waggoner, favorable or not — the story that would live on, the essential story that would survive for posterity, would be the one *she* wrote. What a New York journalist wrote, or one from Detroit or Chicago or Philadelphia or San Francisco, didn't matter from a long-term perspective. The facts as she presented them, however, the account that her readership in Telluride would read, would take its place in the history of her town, and that mattered a great deal. The town and its people had suffered enough and would certainly suffer further. To cast additional shame and pain served no purpose, in Alta's opinion. The town, the people of Telluride, both current and future, didn't need a scapegoat, a villain. They needed a hero. It was her resolve, no matter the uncertainties or ambiguities, that C.D. Waggoner would fill that role.

Anise Koen was not at all certain that she had not lost her sanity. Even after the initial crazed shock of learning that Walter Hillman had taken his own life, a shock that had caused her to believe that she might die of heartbreak and utter despair, there lingered a strong sense that reality, or her perception of it, had drastically and forever altered. She found herself unable to think or speak or simply function as she previously had. Whether there were outward signs of the change in her she did not know, and cared less. Inside, in her heart and in her head, she had been thrown far off kilter, so far that she entertained no notion that the condition might pass. Such an idea did not alarm her. Such emotions as fear or foreboding were no longer available to her. Neither were happiness or hope. Her interior feelings no longer possessed peaks or valleys but were of uniform flatness. Time had also lost its meaning for her. Whether it was day or night or which day of the week, it mattered not the least. Her self-pledge to be vigilant of her diet, to take as much fresh air and exercise as possible, and to engage herself in writing or drawing was broken and forgotten.

The sole factor that served to keep her going on, and which also deepened the suspicion she had in her own sanity, was that Walter was now with her regularly in her cell. He had first come to her on a night before Grant McFerson visited her with his terrible news. It was, she came to know, the night that Walter had shot himself. Then, after McFerson's visit, he had come again. She had been at a pitch of grief that she could not possibly have surmounted, when she felt his presence. It was as black as a tomb in her cell, and her body ached from the sobs and paroxysms that had wracked it for hours. Her mind and her feelings were under siege, and the desperation she felt compared with nothing she had ever known before. Then, she felt him. It was as if he were inside her, his essence somehow mingling with hers, supplanting her grief with his own detachment and peace. Her sobbing stopped and she opened her eyes but, in the dark, could see nothing. Had it been bright daylight, she knew, she would have seen no more. No sound could be heard and she felt nothing physical touch her. Inside, however, she felt changed in a way that she could not have believed possible. Walter was with her, in her; of that she had not the least possible doubt. He had come to be with her, to guard her, understand her, love her. As long as she needed him, she knew he would stay. She knew, too, that her need might last forever.

🏹 🏹 🏹

As soon as Judge Coleman had announced a verdict, C.D. Waggoner experienced a relief not unlike the relief he had felt upon being arrested. It was over now. The days and months and years of strain and worry were truly set free. Rather than dreading the prison sentence that faced him, he was anxious for it to begin. He looked forward to being alone, sequestered, unavailable for the distraught pleadings of borrowers in arrears or the distrustful interrogation of examiners. No longer would he need to worry whether he could keep the bank propped up against the relentless press of hard times. He need no longer fear exposure of his manipulations to bandage the bank together as the town's economic ills infected it fatally and caused it to come apart at the seams. He would miss his walks and cards with his friends. He was sad, immeasurably so, that he had lost his son's respect and trust, perhaps forever. He was sad, too, and devastated, that those who would lose money by the bank's closure might attribute their losses, and the pain and hardship their losses would occasion, to him. There was nothing more to be done about it now, though, not about any of it. The past and the future would forever be inextricably bound — would forever grapple one another like wrestlers locked in combat. The past would always intrude rudely on his future, he knew. But then, it always had. Still, he would not allow himself regret or recrimination. If he had to wrench his thoughts to his order, he would. His happiness would come in recalling the days of old when Telluride had no bellyache and fame and fortune had seemed to be its birthright. All else he would try his best to forget.

The window in Waggoner's New York cell was small and high and had no ledge for pigeons, but he could hear them cooing, their claws scratching the rain gutter and the roof slates above. He had decided that unlike Bulkeley Wells, he did like pigeons. They were simple birds, predictable. They were troubled by no complexity of migrating instinct or outlandish mating ritual. They boasted no elaborate coloration or adornment of feathers, no special ability, unless it be homing. They seemed a plain and honest bird to Waggoner, and he liked that about them. He liked it very much. He hoped there would be pigeons where he was going.

CHAPTER TWENTY

The federal penitentiary in Atlanta was housed in a brick building of imposing stature. It had the look of a Victorian factory and — except for the high walls surrounding it, crested with shards of broken glass and taut strands of barbed wire — it could have been easily mistaken as a place where manufacturing or processing took place, perhaps to do with cotton or tobacco, as fields of both were plentiful in the surrounding area. Tall brick stacks, smoke and steam billowing from them and dissipating lazily into the quiet azure of the Georgian sky, added to the building's industrial appearance. In its stolidity, and in the abruptness by which the building rose up from the flat treeless plain that stretched as far as the eye could see, it was a forbidding place. C.D. Waggoner eyed it warily. It would be his home for the next stretch of years, possibly as many as ten, perhaps fewer if he were granted parole, but certainly no less than six. Six years had been the minimim term he would serve, ordered by Judge Coleman.

Waggoner's hands were cuffed and his ankles shackled, a condition that he had known for what seemed much longer a time than it had actually been. Still, no matter how long, he could never get used to them. They were heavy and awkward, and they hurt. In his case, they were also entirely superfluous. Without them, he would never pose a threat or try to escape. He felt less certain of the risk posed by the other occupant of the police wagon's rear hold, a fellow of brutish features and muscled physique who spoke with such a pronounced southern accent as to be unintelligible. Where Waggoner's cuffs and shackles seemed overly large and cumbrous, the other prisoner's did not, and he seemed as unbothered by them as he would have been by a pair of work gloves or winter leggings. Whether this was a function of habituation or of an obdurate and not very sensitive nature, Waggoner couldn't tell. The expression in the fellow's eyes, almost menacing in its blankness, argued either possibility equally well.

"What're you in for?" the other prisoner had asked, when they had been on the road from the train station for perhaps a quarter of an hour.

Waggoner needed to have the question repeated three times before the words were clear to him. It sounded for all the world as if the man was saying, "Watchin' fur?"

Rather than try to explain the technical counts of his verdict and sentencing, Waggoner kept it short. "Bank robbery," he said, wondering reflexively if that would raise or lower him in the other's estimation.

The man whistled. It was a surprisingly light, sweet note, one that Waggoner would have guessed unlikely to issue from its source, a mouth beaten by poor diet, too much chaw, and the tell-tale insignia of more than a few brawls.

The convict shook his head slowly, a dull, gaping grin on his lumpen face that may or may not have been in place ever since he climbed into the paddy wagon — Waggoner hadn't noticed. The rest of the ride he had said nothing, and asked no more questions, appearing not to expect any from Waggoner. Eventually, he closed his eyes and seemed to drift into sleep. Waggoner, although he was tired and felt as if he hadn't slept properly in weeks, could not achieve the same state. A combination of anticipation and dread informed him with nervous energy and, if not for the heavy irons that pressed on his bones and dug into his skin every time he shifted position, he would have squirmed and fidgeted on his seat.

The police vehicle slowed and its tires crunched on unpaved gravel. It stopped at the prison gate guardhouse, and Waggoner could hear the sound of banter between the guards and the driver. It was only then that he turned in his seat and craned his neck to see out of the small, high window of the hold. The penitentiary, despite its daunting dimension, the dour strictness of its lines, the unrelenting sameness and heaviness of its brickwork, inspired no additional dread in him. What he had expected, he didn't know exactly. Something less monumental, certainly; something less upstanding in appearance, both physically and figuratively. He would not have been surprised to behold a more sprawling and decayed facility, a place of shadows and shabbiness. Those were the sorts of images that had been in his dreams of late. Seeing now the orderliness of the jail, the care with which it had so obviously been constructed and, just as obviously, maintained, provided a feeling of comfort and hope that Waggoner had not anticipated. He would survive this place, he suddenly knew. Until that moment, it had not been a certainty in his mind. Seeing it now, he knew he would adjust to its environment, adapt to its rules, assimilate. He would do nothing to cause affront to anyone. He would be a model prisoner. He would endure.

The paddy wagon pulled ahead slowly from the gatehouse and then stopped again. The driver got out and opened the back doors. Waggoner's companion opened his heavy lids and stood, bent sharply at the waist and neck, the height of the hold inadequate for him. He stepped down from the wagon with nonchalance, as if his hands and feet were unfettered and he was emerging from a company bus to begin a regular day's work. Waggoner, needing barely any adjustment to stand up, tried to effect a similar casualness getting out, but the weight of the manacles and chains made him awkward, and he had none of the other man's physical vigor. He stumbled on landing, tried to compensate, and ended up falling painfully to his knees. Before the driver could make a move to help him, the other prisoner had grabbed the back of his jacket and jerked him up, as if he were no more than a weed growing in the red gravel-strewn dirt.

"Much obliged," he offered.

The big man nodded, the same empty grin still stuck to his face, but said nothing, and in silence they were led into the huge building.

Waggoner took a last sweeping look at the outside world, the unalterating flatness of the penitentiary's surrounds. But he saw no flatness and nothing of the red clay of the soil. Instead, as clearly as if he was standing in the middle of Colorado Avenue, he saw the sharp outlines of the San Juans rising in all directions, their peaks dusted with snow, set off brilliantly against a cobalt blue Colorado sky. In his nostrils, he smelled cool alpine air. He smiled, the same shy smile that he had worn so perenially during his years in Telluride. Following the driver and the other prisoner, he shuffled into the penitentiary and its door thudded heavily shut behind him.

CHAPTER TWENTY-ONE

Montrose, Colorado — 1959

It was an unexpected coincidence, a chance meeting with an old acquaintance, that led to Alta Cassietto corresponding after so many years with Buck Waggoner. She had gone for tea at her friend's home, Betty Ruth Duncan. There was a small group of others there who, like her, had moved down from the Telluride mountains, away from the long harsh winters, the thin air, and the even thinner economy, to live in the comparative mildness and prosperity of Montrose. It was a small reunion and it was staged every few months, a time to catch up, gossip, share reminiscences of the old days in Telluride. Among them they had stories enough to tell for years. And the best ones they were content to retell and hear over and over.

On this occasion, a woman named Dolores Aldasoro was at the gathering. She was now living in Reno and was on her way back there after visiting her family in Telluride. The Aldasoros had been in Telluride as far back as its earliest days. They were sheep ranchers originally from the Basque province of Spain and were now the largest property owners in San Miguel County. Their land, most all of it with southern exposure, stretched for thousands of acres across the flank of the St. Sophia Ridge, a spine of sharp, high peaks that ran on an east-to-west plane. The ridge extended for several miles along the north side of the canyon that boxed in Telluride. Although much of the Aldasoro land was too recalcitrant for farming of any kind, whole expanses of the mesa, level benches formed ten thousand years before by a retreating glacier, had long ago been clear-cut of trees and now provided ample grazing land, its summer grasses rich in nutrients washed down by snowmelt streams and percolated from countless small springs.

Alta had always considered the Aldasoro property the most beautiful in the county, its setting spectacularly majestic, even in a landscape where majesty was commonplace. She was delighted to see

Dolores and they quickly caught up on each other's lives. Owing to the rare event of her visit, Dolores was in much demand at the gathering, and Alta had to be content with the few minutes she managed to have with her in private conversation. As Dolores was being swept away to cakes and catching up with the others, she said, "Oh, by the way. You'll never in a million years guess who I ran into just recently in Reno."

Alta smiled and shook her head in puzzlement.

"C.D. Waggoner. I couldn't have been more shocked if I had seen a ghost."

Then she was pulled playfully away and Alta was left on her own, her mind, just a moment ago quiescent, now alive with thoughts that Waggoner's name never failed to conjure. She longed to pepper Dolores with questions, but the other woman was cornered all evening, first by one person, then another. Eventually, as everyone was leaving, Alta managed to speak with her again briefly.

"Tell you what," said Dolores as her ride honked from the driveway. "Give me your address and I'll write you. I'll tell you what I know, though it isn't much. The only reason I even thought of it was that he specifically asked after you." Then, amid goodbyes called out from all directions, she climbed into the car waiting for her and disappeared down the darkening street.

Some weeks later, Alta received a letter with a Reno postmark. She made herself a cup of tea and settled down at her kitchen table to read it, intrigued to see what news Dolores would provide of Buck Waggoner after so many years. The letter was written in a slanting and careful hand, the script old-fashioned and not easy to read. The greeting was formal. Alta frowned and looked again at the envelope's postmark. Then she turned the letter over. The signature on the bottom was by no means her friend's. She squinted to make it out, but she knew before she had that the letter held more than news of Waggoner: It was news from him.

Alta put the letter down, closed her eyes, and breathed in as if fortifying herself. It was thirty years since she had last seen Waggoner. There had been few days in all that time that she hadn't thought of him or that what he had done hadn't continued to affect her. Indeed, she could attribute much of who she was, what her life had become, directly to Waggoner. And yet, through three decades, notwithstanding what she repeatedly told herself she believed and what she had so often written, she had never been able to fully, finally convince herself of the "true" motives of Waggoner's infamous heist. A private doubt had always lingered.

Alta took the letter up again and simply looked at it a while without reading. It was one thing to have word of Waggoner from a third party, another altogether to hear from him directly. The feeling was not unlike one she had often had when visiting the Lone Tree Cemetery in Telluride, where it seemed to her the history of the town, its chronicle of tragedies and bygone lives, refused the dormancy of the past; a place where the dead and forgotten seemed to clamor silently but strenuously to be alive and remembered.

She took a breath again and read.

Dear Miss Cassietto,

I was delighted to have word of you from Miss Aldasoro and from her to obtain your address. I hope that you will not mind my writing to you. You are one of the few, perhaps the only person, still familiar with my troubled story. So very much has changed since we knew happier days in Telluride, and yet my heart dwells there always. I have nothing but affection for its memories and for those who helped shape them. Among those memories are the kind and supportive words that you have written of me from time to time in the Telluride Journal. *Ever since I left Telluride I have followed as best I could the news of it. One way and another, I was even able to secure a somewhat regular supply of the newspaper that you for so many years edited. I am grateful for your dedication to keeping the town's history alive and the favorable light by which you have chosen to cast me personally.*

I am an old man now, on my last legs, as they say. My eyesight, always poor, has grown worse, and it is all I can do to make out this paper I write on. I hope that you will be able to read my awkward hand. My wife has passed on, and with her, most of the last of my soul. My son I have neither seen nor heard from for many years. At our last meeting, I presented him with my autobiography, a work that I labored over for some years. He showed no desire to have it and, as I later learned from his wife, he destroyed it. Whether he ever read it or not I do not know. I believe not. I wish now that I had had the foresight to make a

copy. I suspect that you, at least, would have been interested in reading it. Its literary merits or demerits aside, I
believe it would have helped you greatly in understanding
the fateful events that served to bind our lives so many
years ago.

Along with my eyesight, my hearing is failing me, else
I would try to arrange to speak to you by telephone. As it
is, the phone hangs on the wall of my kitchen like nothing
more than an ornament. Unless I am standing next to it, I
cannot hear it ring, and if, by chance, I take a call, I hear
nothing but dull and garbled words from the other end,
unless the caller shouts. As I have no one to speak to and
no cause to believe that anyone should be calling me, I no
longer worry about the phone going unanswered. And yet
I would like to be able to converse with you. Blind and
deaf, loved ones all but memories fast fading, I know with
all certainty that my last breath will soon be drawn. I am
unafraid of dying. I doubt that death, even the torments of
Hell, should those be prescribed to me, can match the pain
of ignominy that I have known in this life.

I tire and will close. Please accept my kindest regards.
I will hope to hear from you but will understand if I do not.

Yours,

Charles Waggoner

At the bottom of the page a postscript had been added:

If you have any idea of the fate or whereabouts of Anise
Koen or Bulkeley Wells, I would very much be interested in
knowing them. Buck.

Alta breathed in again deeply; as she did, she realized that she had
been holding her breath the whole time that she had been reading.

She closed her eyes, lost in a thousand thoughts at once, all of
them to do with Telluride, the life that she had lived there, and those
of others before her of whom she had read and written so much. She
had spent the better part of her adult life trying to understand and reconcile in her mind what exactly had happened to turn the exciting,
vibrant, important town that she had so loved into a moribund one of
boarded-up buildings, empty classrooms, forgotten heroes and villains.

She had personally tried her hardest to keep the town alive, to revive it. She worked with the town council to sell Telluride's appeal to tourists. She encouraged everyone on every possible occasion to support local merchants and businesses, rather than buy from catalogues or on monthly excursions to Montrose, where goods and services were, admittedly, more varied and economical. She had entreated countless residents to reconsider their decisions to move away. And she had used her newspaper as a weekly platform to herald Telluride's natural splendor and its grand heritage.

Her efforts were finally in vain. After 1929, the town diminished inexorably, year after year, until even she had been forced to give up hope and join the exodus. Now the town's population was limited to some two or three hundred souls. In the peak years before the turn of the century, twice that many people had lived in Marshall and Savage Basins alone, working just three of the hundreds of mines in the area that produced hundreds of millions of dollars' worth of gold. In the town itself, the population swelled and held for a decade to five thousand or more, people drawn from all over the world and from every walk of life.

Central to what the town had been and to what it became — straddling the good and the bad, as it were — was C.D Waggoner. Whether Telluride could have better survived the onslaught of the Depression, the closure of most of the mines, and the drain of young men to war if Waggoner had not done what he did was an academic question, Alta knew. But that had not stopped her asking it of herself over and over. What she did know, beyond any possible doubt, was that the town's demise had been hastened dramatically after the bank was closed and he was convicted.

Alta got up and went to her desk. She knew that if she didn't answer the unexpected letter straight away, she might never answer it. She knew, too, that she would be forever plagued by regret if she didn't. What she would write, she didn't know. For one thing, she could start by telling Waggoner that she had no idea of Anise Koen's whereabouts. Following her release from jail, she had never returned to Telluride. Her mother had stayed on for some years, but then she, too, had disappeared, leaving no forwarding address. Alta had heard different stories about Anise, but they were vague at best and contradictory at worst. By one account, she had become the moll of a Chicago gangster; by another, the wife of a rich industrialist back East; still a third version had her taking her own life after a series of unhappy and tangled romantic attachments.

Like Waggoner, Anise had long been an enigma to Alta. Her case was not, perhaps, as complicated as his, nor so deeply embedded in the foundation of what Telluride had been and what it came to be, but it mirrored Waggoner's in a way, and her scandal was coincident with his. In fact, the two were intertwined. If Alta was someone, perhaps one of the only people, to whom Waggoner felt he could confide before he breathed his last, then Anise Koen would surely be another. She, like Alta, had shared the cloak of history with Waggoner. Both women, in far different ways, had been wrapped with him in events and consequences that anyone looking from outside, someone who had not worn that shared cloak, could never hope to truly appreciate or understand. Rightly or wrongly, Waggoner had once done all he could for Anise, but his efforts had wrought her no good fortune. Alta had done all she could, as well, for Waggoner. Despite her private doubt, she had consistently portrayed him in favorable terms. The story of C.D. Waggoner that people knew —or would ever come to know, unless someone else told it — was her story. It wasn't necessarily the true story, but it was true enough. More importantly, it was the story that she had once hoped could help her town hold together when nothing else seemed able to do so. As Waggoner's efforts and intentions had ultimately failed Anise, so Alta's had failed. Her rendition of his story had not at all delayed or impeded the town's descent toward oblivion.

As for Bulkeley Wells, she did know his fate. He had descended further and further into financial peril and then ruin, until he could no longer bear the shame of it. At that point, he had put a gun to his head and pulled the trigger.

For an hour, Alta sat occupied with such musings. Again and again she brought her hand to bear on the paper but made no mark, a fresh thought or memory overtaking her, the weight of years and the encompassing reach of history stalling her hand, hampering her intention, confusing her mind. But she had no choice. For her sake no less than Waggoner's, she had to answer his letter and to invite him to write again.

Over the next months, she had four letters from him. The handwriting became increasingly illegible. The letters revealed little apart from his sadness, his abiding love for Telluride, and his gratefulness to her for depicting him to others, and for posterity, as a good man, innocent if not in deed, then at least in motive. He told her nothing much of his life since his Telluride days. She knew from newspaper accounts at the time that he had worked for a while in Grand Junction after his release from jail in the late '30s, dealing cards at a speakeasy owned by Walter "The Big Kid" Eames who, for many years, had operated The Pastime bar next door to the Bank of Telluride. Waggoner's name had appeared in print on the occasion of Eames' murder. He was killed in his club by a shotgun-wielding assassin who fled the scene and was never apprehended. In the ensuing police investigation, Waggoner was indicted for illegal gambling but was never prosecuted. How he came to arrive in Reno, and when, his letters never disclosed. Alta presumed it had been the draw of gaming tables that lured him, though which side of the tables — player's or dealer's — she could only have guessed. Later, she learned from Dolores Aldasoro that Waggoner had worked for most of his years in Reno for the Fuller Brush Company and had even risen to become a territory manager. At first, Alta had had trouble picturing the retiring little man that she remembered knocking on strangers' doors and fast-talking his way inside. But then she realized that he had undoubtedly not opted for the usual, slick, door-to-door tactics but, by his natural deference and gentle manner, had probably succeeded in keeping doors from slamming in his face in a way that more brash and brazen hucksters could not.

To each of his letters she wrote back promptly. Time and again, she resisted her natural and quite urgent temptation to ply him with questions, to try to finally, once and for all, ascertain the full truth of all that he had done and the reasons. After his first letter, she had thought that he wanted to purge his conscience by revealing to her what he perhaps never had to anyone else. But from his ensuing letters, that seemed not to be the case. She surmised that probing with pointed questions would elicit only further pain for him and yield no answers to her. And, of course, it was possible that the whole story, the real story, was as he had repeatedly told it back in 1929, the story that she had decided to accept and promulgate in spite of its obvious discrepancies and her enduring secret doubts.

In his fourth letter, Waggoner inquired of her, rather cryptically, if women were still in the habit of wearing hatpins or if they were something, like so much else that he had known, now out of fashion. She had written back to say that hatpins were, indeed, still generally in vogue. The following week she received a small package in the mail. She recognized the handwriting immediately as Waggoner's. Inside was a hatpin made of gold and adorned with a high-grade nugget. A short note from Waggoner explained that the nugget had been given to him by her father when she was still a little girl. It had come from the Gold King Mine at Alta, where her mother and father had first worked and where they had met. It had been given to Waggoner as a gesture of appreciation for a loan that he had once made to her father when times were tough for him. He hoped that it would be of value to her not as gold, but as a sentiment of thanks and a token of the connection in life between people and generations.

She wrote back thanking him but received no reply. Shortly after sending her the gift, Waggoner died in his home. The exact day and time was unknown. He was discovered by his cleaning woman, who came once a week on Wednesdays. She was likely the last one to have seen him alive the previous week. Dolores Aldasoro wrote Alta that the maid found Waggoner fully dressed and as if asleep in his easy chair, his only expression a small curvature of the lips that looked to be a sad smile.

Alta kept Waggoner's letters awhile and then threw them away. The hatpin she kept and cherished. One day, she thought, if Telluride had managed not to perish altogether and disappear, someone else might happen upon her old idea of writing a proper story about the town's history and about its most notorious citizen. Maybe someone would even look her up one day, in her dotage, to pick her mind about the old days in Telluride and her assessment of the Waggoner case. She chuckled to herself to think what she might say. She wouldn't want to make it too easy for someone, that much was certain. Telluride had never been an easy place: not easy to live and work in, not easy to understand or properly, adequately describe. Anyone who tackled it, in whatever way, would have their work cut out for them. And that was as it should be, she thought. A puzzle is only as worthwhile and rewarding to solve as it is challenging. She would certainly talk to someone if ever they happened along. But, like C.D. Waggoner's letters, she would reveal little, demystify nothing. She would tell the story of the gold hatpin, and show it off, and let it figure as it would in a writer's imagination. More than that, however, she would never offer.

ABOUT THE AUTHOR

Peter Kenworthy was formerly a banker and worked for several years at the Bank of Telluride. He is currently teaching English in China and working on a second novel.

If you enjoyed *Bank Job*, you may like reading these other titles from Western Reflections Publishing Co.:

Salone Italiano: The True Story of an Italian Immigrant Family's Struggles in Southwestern Colorado

Colorado Mountain Women: Tales from the Mining Camps

The Corpse on Boomerang Road: Telluride's War on Labor, 1899-1908

Maggie's Way: The Story of a Defiant Pioneer Woman

Ida: Her Labor of Love

Colorado Mining Stories: Hazards, Heroics, and Humor

A Brief History of Telluride

Father Struck It Rich: Story of the Thomas Walsh Family

Alienation of Affection: Based on the Story of the Sensational 1911 Murder at Denver's Richthofen Castle

To find out more about these titles and others, visit our web site at www.westernreflectionspub.com or call for a free catalog at 1-800-993-4490.